Barometers:

Stick or Cistern Tube

Barometers:
Stick or Cistern Tube

Edwin Banfield

Baros Books

First published 1985

Baros Books
5 Victoria Road
Trowbridge, Wiltshire
BA14 7LH

British Library Cataloguing in Publication Data

Banfield, Edwin
  Barometers: Stick or Cistern Tube
  1. Barometer — History
  I. Title
  681'.2   QC886

ISBN 0-948382-00-7

Typesetting by Avonset, Park House, St. Chads Green, Midsomer Norton, Bath
Illustrations screened by Norton Photo Litho, New Pitt Cottages, Paulton, Bristol
Printed and bound in Great Britain by A. Wheaton & Co. Ltd, Exeter

Contents

Preface   vi

1   Weather Forecasting   1

2   Late Stuart, William & Mary and Queen Anne, 1660–1714   12

3   Early Georgian, 1714–60   29

4   Late Eighteenth Century, 1760–1800   63

5   Regency and William IV, 1800–37   91

6   Victorian, 1837–1901   120

7   Angle Tube Barometers   140

8   Marine Barometers   163

9   Standard, Station and Scientific Barometers   181

10   Mountain and Balloonist's Barometers   194

11   Double- and Multiple-tube Barometers   206

12   Sympiesometers   214

13   Admiral Fitzroy Barometers   220

14   Other Cistern Barometers   234

15   Care of the Stick or Cistern Tube Barometer   240

Bibliography   243

Index   244

Preface

This book, together with its two companion books, *Barometers: Wheel or Banjo* and *Barometers: Aneroid and Barographs*, form an extended and more comprehensive version of my book *Antique Barometers: an Illustrated Survey* published in 1976. It is written around various private and museum collections of barometers and others I have seen or handled over a number of years.

I have not attempted to cover the more technical aspects of barometers but have tried to collate, in an easily readable form, information on English barometers and their makers, obtained from a large number of sources, outlining the history of their development.

The main purpose of this book is to widen understanding and appreciation of the barometer, and to assist the person who possesses or wishes to acquire one. It may also help the small collector and the antique dealer who, in the past, has hesitated to stock them, feeling that he or she had insufficient knowledge of their construction.

Most barometers are attractive pieces of furniture that would grace any hall or living-room, and collecting them is a practical proposition as most are neither large nor heavy and require little or no attention. Unlike other furniture, they take up no floor space and anyone with an eye for beauty of line and grace of proportion cannot but admire the early stick barometers.

In addition to being an object of beauty, the barometer is functional and is always ready to disclose the likely course of the weather for the ensuing hours. A further attraction is that almost all are engraved with the maker's or retailer's name and often his address so that it is possible, by a little research, to discover its approximate age and, sometimes, interesting information about the makers who were, originally, mathematical, optical or philosophical instrument-makers or clockmakers.

Almost all the types of barometers illustrated in this book were produced in sufficient numbers to make them available for purchase, from time to time, at auctions or in antique shops, although late seventeenth and early eighteenth-century specimens are becoming increasingly difficult to find, as they continue to be acquired by collectors both in this country and abroad.

Readers may find various errors and omissions in the text and it is possible that some of the dates attributed to the barometers will be questioned. If there is any evidence available to show that I am in error in any respect, I should appreciate being advised.

I have used far more illustrations than is necessary to trace the history and development of the barometer, so that readers can see the very extensive variety of instruments produced and appreciate that it is unlikely for a collector or dealer to find two barometers that are exactly the same. Because of this, not all the barometers are referred to in the text but the captions have been extended where appropriate.

I am grateful to all those who have provided photographs, which are acknowledged in the captions; I should also like to thank Ros Banfield for typing the manuscript and my daughter Sue Banfield for editing it.

There is a glamour about the past which has a romantic appeal and this, no doubt, is the reason why the impulse to collect antiques is so strong in the individual. Barometers are attractive and useful instruments to collect and I hope this book will stimulate interest in them.

E.B.

1

Weather Forecasting

It can be assumed that weather forecasting began in prehistoric times when human intelligence developed to the extent that man appreciated that his comfort and well-being depended on a sympathetic combination of sunshine, wind and rain. The prehistoric hunting and food gathering way of life was closely dependent upon the vagaries of the weather and people gradually developed an almost intuitive feeling for atmospheric conditions. Early weather lore embodied the collective experience of countless generations of prehistoric hunters, herdsmen, farmers, mariners and others who all led outdoor lives; this was passed from one generation to another orally and later became preserved in a literary form.

Amateur forecasting continued down the ages by studying the sun, the moon and the clouds. The leaves on certain trees and berries in the hedgerows were observed, whilst the behaviour of birds and animals was carefully monitored in the belief that they had a better knowledge of the coming weather than human beings themselves.

From these observations numerous maxims evolved over the centuries and are still repeated today. For example:

Red sky at night, shepherd's delight,
Red sky in the morning, shepherd's warning.

This would appear to have been taken from the Bible as in Matthew XVI, verses 2 and 3, Christ is reported to have declared:

When it is evening, ye say, it will be fair weather for the sky is red. And in the morning it will be foul weather today for the sky is red and lowering.

Birds have also contributed:

Swallows high, staying dry,
Swallows low, wet 'twill blow.

and even the fly was regarded as a natural barometer:

If a fly lands on your nose, swat it till it goes,
If the fly then lands again, it will bring heavy rain.

1

Fig. 1   Galileo Galilei (1564–1642).

In 1579 the herbalist Gerard wrote of the scarlet pimpernel:

The closing of its flowers betokeneth rain and foul weather; contrari-
wise, if they are spread abroad, fine weather.

It is known that the pimpernel, daisy, chickweed and other flowers do indeed
close their petals when the humidity of the air reaches 82 per cent. When rain
is on the way the humidity frequently reaches this level so there are certainly
grounds for the pimpernel's reputation.

The English have always appeared to have a strange preoccupation with
the weather; indeed, many foreigners would claim that the weather is the
Englishman's sole topic of conversation. It is therefore not surprising that an
English meteorologist, William Merle, has the distinction of being the author
of the earliest known systematic weather diary which extends from January
1337 to January 1344 (now preserved in Oxford). He also wrote a comprehensive treatise on predicting the weather using a variety of sources.

Instrumental meteorological observations began early in the seventeenth
century with the invention of the thermometer by Galileo Galilei (*Fig.* 1)
shortly after 1600. The device should, perhaps, have been called a thermo-
baroscope as it was an unsealed instrument and responded to atmospheric

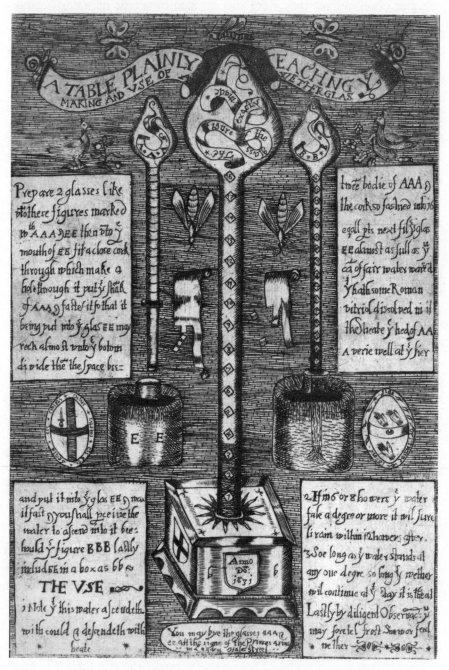

Fig. 2   How to make and use a weather-glass, 1631 (*The British Library*).

3

pressure as well as to temperature. Astronomers, and other scientists, laid the foundations of meteorology as an exact science by making systematic weather observations; they were also assisted by a type of water weather-glass which was in common use around 1630.

Fig. 2 shows an engraving of an advertisement in 1631 setting out the way to make such a weather-glass with water in which Roman Vitriol (copper sulphate) has been dissolved. The instructions tell us that:

1. Note that this water ascendeth with cold and descendeth with heat.
2. If in six to eight hours the water falls a degree or more it will surely rain within 12 hours after.
3. So long as the water stands at any one degree so long the weather will continue to stay where it is. Lastly by diligent observations you may foretell frost, snow or foul weather.

The print advertises that the glasses may be bought at the sign of the Princes Arms in Leadenhall Street.

These instructions were not satisfactory as water was not a suitable liquid, being subject to rapid expansion, evaporation and easily frozen. These instruments could not be described as barometers as the sole purpose of a barometer is to measure the weight of the atmosphere. The word 'barometer' is derived from the Greek word 'baros' meaning 'weight'.

The barometer was invented by an Italian, Evangelista Torricelli (*Fig.*3), who was born in Faenza, Italy in 1608. When he was about 20 he went to the University of Rome to study under Castelli, a scientist. He became a mathematician and was very impressed by the writings of Galileo. Galileo was the first astronomer to use the telescope for studying the sun, the moon and the stars; he was also responsible for the pendulum's laws, was founder of the science of mechanics and laid the foundations of modern physics and astronomy. The two men must have become acquainted because in 1641, at the invitation of Galileo, Torricelli moved to Florence to live and work with him. Galileo was then aged 77 and completely blind; regrettably, the associa-tion was shortlived as Galileo died three months later and Torricelli succeeded him as mathematician and philosopher to the Grand Duke Ferdinand II.

Amongst Galileo's papers Torricelli found various notes on incompleted studies. One which interested him related to water, which, it appeared, could not be raised more than 33 feet with a single-stage suction pump. To reduce the size of the apparatus Torricelli experimented in 1643 with mercury. He took a glass tube approximately 36 inches long and filled it with mercury; he then placed a finger over the open end of the tube and inserted it into a container of mercury. On removing his finger he found that the tube remained full of mercury to a height of about 29 inches above the surface of the mercury in the container. Further experiments soon proved that the weight of the column of mercury was proportionate to the pressure of the air outside the tube.

Fig. 3 Evangelista Torricelli (1608–47).

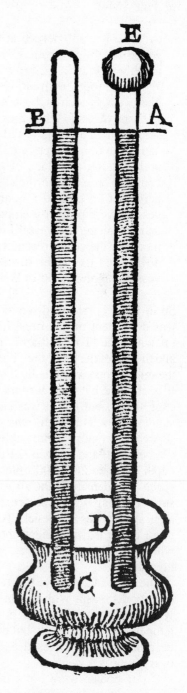

Fig. 5 Robert Boyle (1627–91).

Fig. 4 Torricelli's experiment (*Science Museum, London*).

5

Torricelli described the experiments in a letter to Michelangelo Ricci dated 11 June 1644:

. . . We live submerged at the bottom of an ocean of elementary air, which is known by incontestible experiments to have weight, and so much weight, that the heaviest part near the surface of the earth weighs about one four-hundredth as much as water . . . We have made many glass vessels such as those shown at A and B, wide, and with necks two ells long [*Fig.*4]. When these were filled with quicksilver, their mouths stopped with the finger, and then turned upside-down in a vase C which had some quicksilver in it, they were seen to empty themselves, and nothing took the place of the quicksilver in the vessels which were being emptied. Nevertheless the neck A D always remained full to the height of an ell and a quarter and a finger more. To show that the vessels were perfectly empty, the vase was filled up to D with water; and on raising the vessel little by little, it was observed that when the mouth of the vessel reached the water, the quicksilver in the neck came down, and the water rushed in with horrible violence and filled the vessel completely up to E . . .

So in 1643 Torricelli discovered that the height of the mercury in the tube was dependent on the pressure of the atmosphere. This has since become known as the 'Torricellian Experiment' and the space between the mercury and the top of the tube, the 'Torricellian Vacuum'. Torricelli was developing the microscope when he died of a fever in Florence in 1647 at the age of 39. It is claimed by some writers that Torricelli did not himself undertake the experiment, but that it was carried out by his close friend, Viviani, at the suggestion of Torricelli, who explained to him exactly what would happen.

Air is a mixture of invisible gases composed almost entirely of nitrogen (78 per cent) and oxygen (21 per cent). It envelopes the earth's surface to a depth of some 200–300 miles, submerging the earth and isolating it from space. The density of the air varies with increase of distance from the earth's surface, being lightest at its extreme height and becoming denser and heavier as it approaches sea level. Towards the surface, the atmosphere becomes more disturbed, turbulent and variable in character, giving a layer of air which is subject to storms, changes of wind, temperature, pressure and humidity.

The layer of air above this region is calmer and becomes more so as the air density decreases with height. The only storms are of an electrical nature, while high winds prevail at certain altitudes, and there are changes of temperature horizontally but not vertically. Still further from the surface, air becomes less compressed and less dense, until there is no air at all and everything is a vacuum.

If our bodies were not constructed so that the air and fluids within us pressed outwards with equal force to balance the pressure outside, we should be crushed by the weight of the air of almost 15 tons exerted on the average adult. The downward force of the atmosphere is about 14.7 pounds per

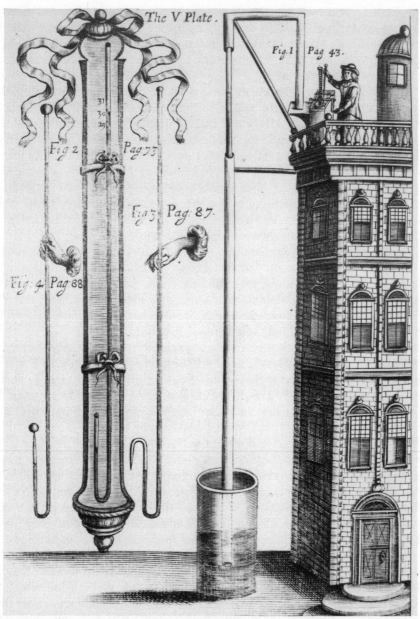

Fig. 6   Robert Boyle's siphon barometer and water barometer, 1669 (*The British Library*).

square inch at sea level; this decreases to about 7 pounds at 20,000 feet above sea level. Mercury is 10,784 times heavier than air.

Although it is generally accepted that Torricelli invented the barometer, it was René Descartes (1596–1650), a French philosopher and physicist, who first added a paper scale to the Torricelli tube in 1648. His research, in conjunction with a contemporary French physicist, Blaise Pascal (1623–62), was mainly concerned with measuring different heights by recording differences in air pressure.

Robert Boyle (*Fig.* 5) appears to have been the first person to introduce the barometer to England. He was a prolific author, writing on science, philosophy and theology. He was a student in Italy during the period of the Torricellian Experiment and studied the writings of Galileo. On his return to England, he established a private laboratory in Oxford and undertook his own experiments, proving that the phenomenon of Torricelli's experiment was, indeed, caused by air, that sound was impossible in a vacuum, that air was necessary for life and flame and that air was permanently elastic. He developed this discovery into a quantitative relationship that volume varies inversely with pressure. This is known as 'Boyle's Law'.

He developed the experiment into a practical barometer, or baroscope as it was then called, by being the first to use a graduated scale to record the height of the mercury in the tube; these are now known as register plates. *Fig.* 6 shows Boyle's siphon barometer and water barometer from his 'Continuation of New Experiments Physico-Mechanical touching the Spring and Weight of the Air, and their Effects' (Oxford, 1669).

Since the vacuum in the inverted tube gives no resistance, any change in atmospheric pressure varies the height of the mercury in the tube. In England the average height of the mercury column is a little under 30 inches at sea level at a temperature of 32 degrees Fahrenheit and at a latitude of about 50 degrees. Nearer the equator the mean height is greater, whilst nearer the poles it is less.

When it was discovered that the variations in the height of mercury gave an indication as to the possible changes in the weather, an attempt was made from recorded observations to deduce the height of the mercury applicable to a particular weather condition. It was found that on fine, sunny days the mercury stood generally above 30 inches, whilst on days when the weather was changeable it was usually between 29 and 30 inches; on dull, rainy days it was often below 29 inches. Because of these conclusions it became the practice to engrave the words, Fair, Changeable, Rain etc. on the register plates in addition to the height from 28 to 31 inches. These weather indications are often unreliable guides as humidity, temperature, wind direction and height of the barometer above sea level are other important factors that determine the height of the mercury. They can be looked upon as rough guides, but it is the movement of the mercury, up or down, rather than its actual height, which foretells changes in the weather.

An important event in the development of meteorology and horology was the formation in 1660 of the Royal Society for the Improvement of Natural Knowledge. Charles II, who was fascinated by scientific experiments, became its patron and granted it a Royal Charter in 1662. The Society encouraged an all-embracing spirit of enquiry with its members, mainly scientists, interested in establishing the natural laws of the universe; they were also dedicated to finding practical solutions to everyday problems and many of their discoveries had an important bearing on domestic life.

The name of the Society was shortened later to the Royal Society and Robert Hooke, who invented the wheel barometer, was its first Curator of Experiments in 1662 when he was aged only 23.

Joseph Glanvill, a leading anglican theologian, was a Fellow of the Royal Society and did much to publicise the new experimental science and asserted its compatibility with religion. In 1668 he wrote 'Plus Ultra or the Progress and Advancement of Knowledge Since the Days of Aristotle', and his comments on the barometer are interesting:

The Barometer is another late Instrument very helpful to Useful Knowledge. That there is gravity even in the Air itself, and that that Element is only comparatively light, is now made evident and palpable by Experience, though Aristotle and his Schools held a different Theory: And by the help of Quicksilver in a Tube, the way is found to measure all the degrees of Compression in the Atmosphere, and to estimate exactly any accession of weight, which the Air receives from Winds, Clouds or Vapours. To have said in Elder Times, That Mankind should light upon an Invention whereby those Bodies might be weigh'd, would certainly have appeared very wild and extravagant, and it will be so accounted for some time yet, till men have been longer and are better acquainted with this instrument. . . . [People have always scoffed at new theories and inventions] . . . But Experience turns the laugh upon the confident incredulity of the Scoffer; and he that will not believe, needs no more for his conviction, than the labour of a Tryal. Let them then fill a Tube of Glass of some feet in length, with Quicksilver; and having sealed one end, let him stop the other with his Finger, and immerse that which is so stop'd into a Vessel of Mercury, the Tube being perpendicularly erected; let him then subtract his finger, and he will perceive the Quicksilver to descend from the tube into the subjacent vessel, till it comes to 29 digits or thereabouts; there, after some Vibrations, it ordinarily rests. The reason that this remainder of the Mercury does not descend also, is, because such a Mercurial Cylinder is just equiponderant to one of the incumbent Atmosphere that leans upon the Quicksilver in the Vessel, and so hinders a further descent. It is concluded therefore, that such a Cylinder of the Air as presses upon the Mercury in the Vessel, is of equal weight to about 29 Digits of that ponderous Body in the Tube. Thus it is when the Air is in its ordinary temper: but Vapours, Winds and Clouds alter the Standard, so that the Quicksilver sometimes falls, sometimes rises in the Glass, proportionably to the greater or less accession of gravity and compression the Air hath received from any of those alterations; and the Degree of increase beyond the Standard is the measure of the

9

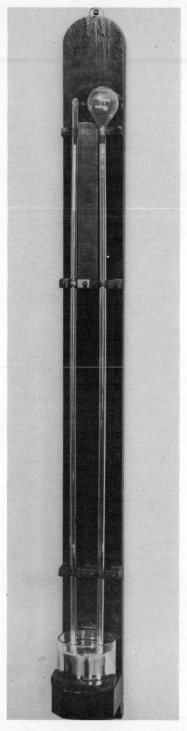

Fig. 7 Copy of first Torricelli barometer (British Crown Copyright, *Science Museum, London*).

additional gravity. This Experiment was the Invention of Torricellius, and used to little more purpose at first, but to prove a Vacuum in Nature; and the deserted part of the Glass-Tube was by many thought an absolute void, which I believe is a mistake: But it hath been since improved to his Design of weighing the degrees of compression in the Air; a thing that may signifie much in giving us to understand its temper in several Places, as Hills and in Caves, in divers Regions and Climates, which may lend to the disclosing many excellent Theories and helps in humane Life. And the Air is so Catholick a Body, and hath so great an influence upon all others, and upon ours, that the advantage of such an Instrument, for the better acquainting us with its nature, must needs be very considerable, and a good Aid to general Philosophy. And who yet knows how far, and to what Discoveries this Invention may be improved? . . . The Royal Society, by their Care and Endeavours in the using this Instrument, give us hopes, that they will let none of its useful Applications to escape us. And I know not whether we may not mention it as the first great benefit we have from it, that it was an occasion of the Invention of Mr. Boyle's famous Pneumatick Engine: . . .

From around 1660 the barometer was developed as an instrument mainly for the measurement of heights and only gradually did meteorologists realise that it could be useful as an aid to weather forecasting. The earliest barometers were made to the order and design of scientists by clockmakers and instrument-makers, with all the metalwork heavily gilded to avoid polishing, essential with other metals, which might shake the mercury and lead to the intrusion of air bubbles into the tube. Barometers were not made for domestic use until around 1670.

In 1674 George Ravenscroft developed and patented a tough clear glass which assisted in the production of barometer tubes; they could then be drawn into a hollow tube with a one-tenth of an inch bore.

Barometers, probably similar to the illustration in *Fig*. 7, could certainly be purchased in 1675, as in that year a Richard Legh of Lyme Hall, Cheshire, wrote to his wife while he was in London: 'The carrier will bring a long deale box that hath quicksilver in itt. Prithee command that there be great care of itt, that neither of them — the box or bottle — be stirred till I come home. Tis a device I had of Sir Jonas Moore to know the weather by.'

Jonas Moore (1627–79) was a lecturer in mathematical sciences and supplied his pupils with books and instruments from the Tower of London where he lived. He made the Tower a centre of scientific observation, mathematical practice and patronage. In 1673 he was appointed Surveyor of Ordnance, and elected a Fellow of the Royal Society in 1674.

The early domestic barometers were of simple construction and were subsequently discarded by owners, when broken or otherwise, as more sophisticated types in attractive cases became available. It is not, therefore, surprising that none of the earliest, made before 1680, appears to have survived.

2

Late Stuart, William & Mary and Queen Anne, 1660–1714

It is not known exactly when barometers were first made for sale to the general public but they do not appear to have been available in London shops much before 1680.

Francis North (1637–85), Baron of Guildford and a Lord Chancellor, seems to have been responsible for encouraging the serious production of barometers around 1675, according to his brother, Roger North. The following passage is from Roger's 'Life of the Rt. Hon. Francis North, Baron Guildford, etc.', published in 1742.

His Lordship was much affected by the discoveries, which fell in the consequences of the Torricellian Experiment; whereby a new world of air, compressing every thing it touches, is revealed. He could not but observe a manifest connection between the alterations of the mercurial station, and the course of the winds and weather; but could not fix in his mind any certain rules of indication, but rather the contrary, viz. that events failed as often as corresponded with the ordinary expectation. But yet he would not give it over for desperate, and hoped that a more general observation might generate a better prognostic of the weather from it, than was yet known. And that must be expected from a more diffused, if not an universal, use of it, which could not then be thought of; because the instruments were rare, and confined to the cabinets of the virtuosi; and one was not to be had but by means of some of them. Therefore his Lordship thought fit to put some ordinary tradesmen upon making and selling them in their shops; and accordingly he sent for Henry Jones, the clock-maker in the Inner-Temple Lane; and, having shown him the fabrick, and given him proper cautions in the erecting of them, recommended the setting them forth for sale in his shop; and, it being a new thing, he would certainly find customers. He did so, and was the first person that exposed the instrument to sale publickly in London. But his Lordship, perceiving that his business lay in other operations he was more used to, and that he began to slight these, sent for Mr. Winn, a famous Instrument-maker, over-against his house in Chancery Lane, and did the like to him, who pursued the manufacturing to great perfection, and to his own no small advantage; and then others took it up, and few clock-makers, instrument-makers, cabinet-makers, and diverse other trades, were without them always in their shops, ready for sale: And all moving from the first essays, as I related, set on foot by his Lordship.

It is perhaps understandable that Henry Jones was not particularly interested in making barometers because he was, at that time, already famous as a watch- and clockmaker.

Henry Winn, or Wynn as he was generally known, was apprenticed to Ralph Greatorex, a mathematical instrument-maker, in 1654; he became a member of the Clockmakers' Company in 1662 and a Master in 1690. He was a renowned instrument-maker and furnished 'Any sort of mathematical instruments whether for sea or land' at his shop 'near the Sugar Loaf' in Chancery Lane, London. He was particularly noted for his magnetic needles, compasses of various types and he made a pendulum watch, with shagreen case, for the King.

One of the first barometers produced for the domestic market and signed by Henry Wynne is illustrated in *Fig.* 8. It was made around 1680 and the case is of oak veneered with walnut in sections of 4–5 inches up the case. The veneer, which was then called 'faneer' because the slices of wood were cut across the grain to show the 'fan' of the timber, was split in half with the matching halves applied to each side of the tube to give a balanced effect. The plain, but attractive, case is 41 inches high and 4 inches wide with a domed and moulded hood. The cistern cover is of solid walnut with the top section removable so that mercury can be poured into the glass bowl or cistern contained within it.

The register plates are of silvered brass and decorated with engraved flower heads and entwined leaves, whilst the edges of the plate are adorned with a wheat-ear design popular until the middle of the eighteenth century. The weather indications are in English Roman seventeenth-century capitals and minuscules, or as the printers call them, lower-case letters. The spelling is interesting:

Sumer.	**Winter.**
Setled.	Hard.
Cleare.	Frosts.
Dry.	Cold.
Chang:	-able.
Rain.	Snow.
M^{ch}. Rain.	M^{ch}. Snow.
Stormy.	Weather.
Henry	Wynne.

A sickle-shaped recording pointer is fixed in the groove on the right-hand side register plate and this has to be adjusted manually. For protection, the

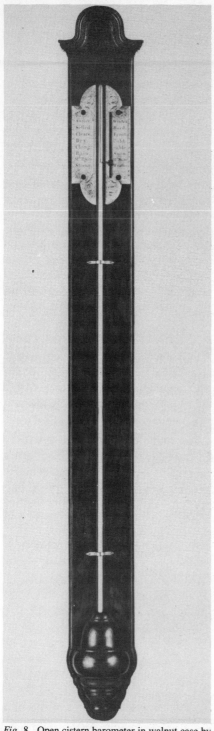

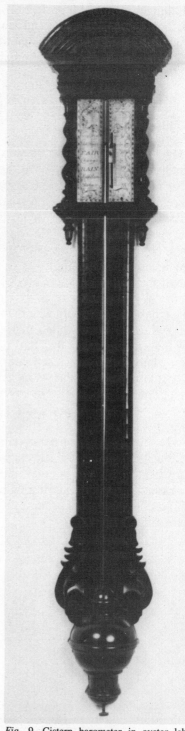

Fig. 8 Open cistern barometer in walnut case by Henry Wynne, c. 1680.

Fig. 9 Cistern barometer in oyster laburnum case. Unsigned, c. 1695 (*Park Street Antiques, Berkhamstead*).

14

Fig. 10 Detail of *Fig.* 9.

15

tube is set in a deep groove down the case and is held in position by two brass loops which are not original.

Considerable insight into the design and construction of barometers of this period is afforded by John Smith, clockmaker, who in 1688 published 'A Complete Discourse of the Nature, Use and Right Managing of that Wonderful Instrument the Baroscope or Quicksilver Weather Glass'. Of the cistern barometer he tells us that:

The Baroscope or Quick-silver Weather Glass is composed and made up of the following parts. First the Frame or main Body of the Instrument. Secondly a Glass Tube or Pipe. Thirdly a Cistern or Receiver. Fourthly Two Register Plates, with a Sliding Index, and lastly a sufficient Quantity of Quick-silver to fill the tube, and adjust the Receiver.

Of the Frame − The Frame is Wood, of which any sort may serve, but for Ornament sake, the Choicest are generally made use of, such as Ebony, Walnut or Olive-Wood. The Shape and Figure is various according to the Fancies of Them that either make or use them; but for the Size that must always be such that the length may admit a Glass-Tube of at least three Foot Long and its Breadth sufficient to affix thereon the Register Plates.

In the middle of this Frame must be cut out a half-round Groove or Channel, throughout the whole Length of it, and of such a Depth as may be sufficient to secure the Tube, when set in it from being broken by any outward Accident.

Near the Bottom of the Frame is to be affixed the Cistern-Box and Cover of such a Size and Bigness as may admit a Glass Cistern of Three Inches Diameter, or three and a half, and one Inch in Height at least.

Lastly upon the upper part of the Frame are to be affixed the two Register-Plates, in doing of which you must observe a due Distance between the Lowest Division on the Registers, and the Bottom of the Cistern-Box.

From 1660 to 1720 walnut was considered the standard material for all the finest quality furniture, and it is not surprising that virtually all the extant barometers of this period are made or veneered with walnut. Clocks and barometers became more fashionable towards the end of the seventeenth century, mainly due to the influence of Charles II who patronised the arts and encouraged innovation and trade.

Barometers were popular in the context of furniture design and their cases followed closely the form of contemporary clock cases until the middle of the eighteenth century; this was, no doubt, due to the many clockmakers who diversified into barometer-making.

Such a barometer is shown in *Figs.* 9 and 10 where the clockmakers' influence can be clearly seen. It has an oak case veneered with oyster laburnum which was the preferred alternative to walnut. The edges of the frame are moulded and the scrolls above the solid walnut cistern cover have

Fig. 11 Open cistern barometer in walnut case. Unsigned, c. 1695.   *Fig.* 12 Open cistern barometer in walnut and sycamore case, c. 1695 (*Park Street Antiques, Berkhamstead*).   *Fig.* 13 Open cistern barometer in walnut with marquetry decoration. Unsigned, c. 1700 (*G. E. Marsh, Winchester*).

open fretwork. This type of scrollwork was not used in the eighteenth century, and as the barley-sugar-twist turned pillars housing the register plates are similar to those used on clocks around 1690, the barometer can safely be dated c. 1695. *Fig.* 10 shows in detail the domed and moulded hood, also the silvered brass register plates decorated with leaf and scroll designs and wheat-ear border. The winter weather indications have been dispensed with in favour of a 3 inch scale and the original sickle-shaped pointer has been replaced by a vernier. The weather indications are in English Roman seventeenth-century italics. The barometer has been converted from an open cistern type to a boxwood closed cistern as evidenced by the adjustable screw below the cistern cover; this type of cistern will be discussed below.

A rather more ornate barometer of similar date is illustrated in *Fig.* 11. The oak case is veneered with walnut and a decorative hood is mounted above the register plates which increases the overall height to 47 inches. A wedge-shaped section of the moulded cornice below the register plates can be lifted out to allow the tube to be removed.

Fig. 12 depicts a similar type of barometer in a carved walnut case veneered with sycamore. The broken pediment is typical of the cornices seen on bookcases and cabinets around 1700. The pillars housing the register plates are fluted and reeded, whilst the tube is protected with a sheath of walnut. An interesting feature is the half-inch slots through which the four screws retain the two register plates; this is to allow the plates to be raised or lowered, within the half-inch limit, so as to adjust the scale reading if it is too high or too low when compared with other barometers.

With the accession of William III and Mary of Holland to the throne of England in 1689 there was a marked influence from the Continent on the design of English furniture. The King brought with him craftsmen skilled in the art of furniture manufacture and the Dutch influence in particular was seen in the shape and decoration of the better quality pieces. The Dutch were masters in marquetry and this form of decoration was popular on clocks and barometers during the first quarter of the eighteenth century.

Fig. 13 shows an open cistern barometer with the frame veneered in walnut with marquetry decoration consisting of leaves and flowers. Woods used in this period for marquetry included chestnut, holly, laburnum, fruitwoods, yew, box, pine, sycamore and lignum-vitae. Sometimes these woods — including walnut — were bleached, dyed or faded to increase the colour contrasts. This barometer was made around 1700; note that the fretwork above the cistern covers on the barometers in *Figs.* 9–12 has now been discontinued in favour of solid wood scrollwork. The silvered brass register plates have the weather indications for summer and winter.

By far the most prolific and interesting of the early domestic barometer-makers was John Patrick. He was apprenticed to a joiner, William Tompson, in 1686 for seven years and appears to have specialised in making barometers, as an instrument-maker, from the time he completed his apprenticeship in 1693. He soon became accepted as the leading maker of his day and traded from Ship Court in the Old Bailey, London. From his own research and observations, he published 'Rules and Observations on the Various Rising and Falling of the Mercury to foreknow the Weather by the Barometer'. When repeating these rules in his *Lexicon Technicum* in 1704, John Harris described Patrick as the 'Torricellian Operator' and added:

> I think myself obliged in justice to tell the world that I have never seen better Weather Glasses of all kinds made any where than by Mr. Patrick; who doth really deserve all possible encouragement for the many experiments he hath made in order to improve the Barometer, and which he is always willing to shew to all ingenious and curious persons.

As well as selling barometers direct to the public, Patrick sold them to other instrument-makers and retailers. Records show that his barometers were sold by John Marshall, John Yarwell, George Graham, and Daniel Quare. Many of his barometers were unsigned, and he could have made some of those already described.

The main disadvantage of the open cistern tube barometer was the difficulty in moving it from place to place. Unless it was carried very carefully in an upright position, the mercury in the glass cistern could easily be spilt and this could allow air to enter the tube and so distort the reading. The air would gradually rise to the top of the mercury and enter the vacuum which would, again, give a false reading. Another hazard was that if the tube were quickly inclined away from the vertical, the mercury would rise to the top of the tube with such force that it could break the glass.

Several makers gave thought to this problem and various remedies were tried. By constricting the bore of the top inch or so of the tube the upward surge of the mercury could be contained and so prevent breakages. It was also possible to prevent the mercury from being spilt by covering the open cistern with leather firmly fixed from the brim across to the tube.

These refinements did not make the barometer really portable, and there is considerable doubt as to whether John Patrick or Daniel Quare made the first truly portable barometer. The benefit of the doubt must be given to Daniel Quare because he was able to satisfy the Patent Office who granted him a patent on the 2 August 1695 giving protection to 'A portable weather glass or barometer, which may be removed and carried to any place though turned upside-down without spilling one drop of the quicksilver or letting any air into the tube, and that nevertheless the air shall have the same liberty to operate upon it as on those common ones now in use with respect to atmosphere'.

The Clockmakers' Company, of which Quare was a member, opposed the granting of the patent, as it was against the exclusive possession of a trading right, and resolved to defend any member of the Company – or John Patrick who was not a member, but assisted the Company – if suits of law were brought against them for making portable barometers. However, the patent was granted and no litigation appears to have ensued, although Quare's cistern was soon imitated and improved.

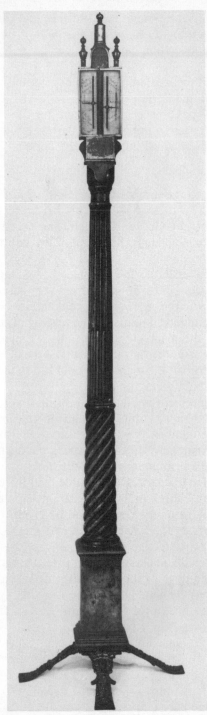

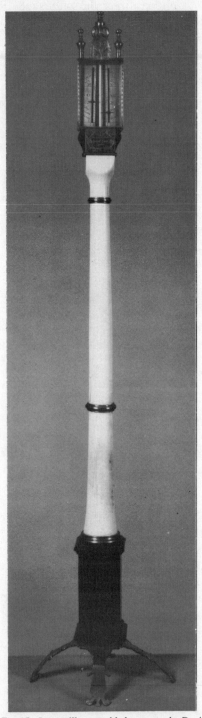

Fig. 14 Walnut pillar portable barometer by Daniel Quare, London, c. 1700 (British Crown Copyright, *Science Museum, London*).

Fig. 15 Ivory pillar portable barometer by Daniel Quare, c. 1700 (Crown Copyright, *Victoria and Albert Museum, London*).

20

Fig. 16   Detail of *Fig.* 15.

The patent details gave no specification of the Quare portable barometer, but this can be established by examining his early instruments, many of which still survive. He made use of the fact that air could permeate leather and substituted the glass cistern for a leather bag, the top of which he cemented to the glass tube, so forming a closed cistern. The leather bag was housed in a cistern box with the base of the bag resting on a padded screw, which operated through a nut set in the bottom of the cistern box. When the screw was advanced it raised the leather bag and reduced the volume of the cistern until the cistern and tube were full of mercury. The barometer could then be turned upside-down and carried at will, without adverse effect. When transferred to its new position it could easily be set up for operation again by withdrawing the screw to its original position.

Daniel Quare, who was born in 1649, was a Quaker and became one of the outstanding watch- and clockmakers of all time. He invented the repeating watch around 1680 and became a Master of the Clockmakers' Company in 1708; he was also an instrument-maker, who specialised in barometers, making basically two types with portable cisterns.

One, a walnut pillar portable barometer made around 1700, is shown in *Fig.* 14. It has a squared cistern cover with the lower section of the case twisted whilst the upper half is fluted and reeded. The register plates are of silvered brass and enclosed in a gilt brass box with a glass front. The large central finial contains the top of the tube, and the knobs on the top of the two smaller finials operate a mechanism to adjust the two recording pointers set in grooves on the register plates. The feet are of brass, decorated with a chased moulding of foliate design, and are hinged so that they can be retracted to hang downwards if it is desired to hang the barometer on a wall. The front foot hides the portable screw. The weather indications below the engraved hood are the same as those shown in *Fig.* 16, and these appear to be standard on Quare barometers. The plate below the register-plate box is engraved 'Invented and Made by Dan Quare, London'. It is numbered '38' on the right-hand side of the box enclosing the register plates.

Figs. 15 and 16 illustrate a similar Quare barometer except that it has a plain ivory pillar mounted on an ebonised wooden cistern cover. The brass feet are without decoration. Quare gave serial numbers to some of his models; this barometer is numbered '148' at the top of the right-hand face of the signature square.

A particularly interesting Quare barometer is shown in *Fig.* 17. The plain turned ivory case is in four parts, which is the usual form of construction for an ivory pillar, but in addition to the English weather indications on the front register plates, there is a second set of register plates on the reverse side giving the indications in French. The second set was incorporated so that the barometer could be exported to France, and to allow the choice of plates there is a reversible hanging device in the form of a ring immediately below the register-plate box. The ring can be made to swivel, reversing a projection that fixes to a wall hook. This barometer has a particularly tall central finial, making it approximately 40 inches high.

The other type of barometer made by Quare is called a pendant portable

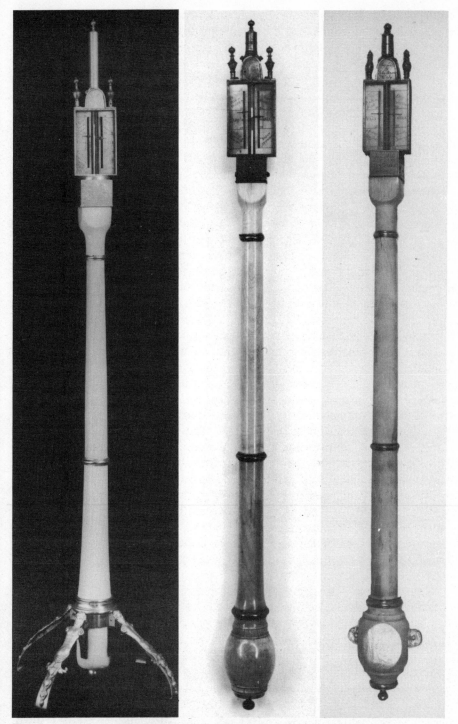

Fig. 17 Ivory pillar portable barometer by Daniel Quare, c. 1700 (*Hotspur Ltd, London*). *Fig.* 18 Ivory pendant portable barometer by Daniel Quare, c. 1700 (*Christies, London*). *Fig.* 19 Ivory pendant portable barometer by Daniel Quare, c. 1700 (*G. E. Marsh, Winchester*).

23

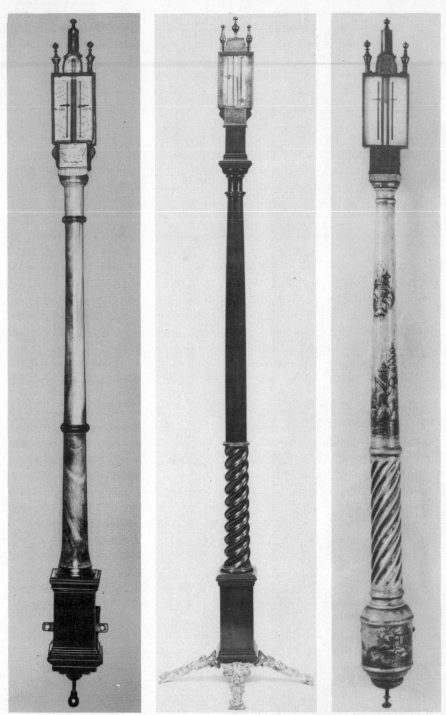

Fig. 20 Walnut and ivory pendant portable barometer by Daniel Quare, c. 1700 (*G. E. Marsh, Winchester*). *Fig.* 21 Walnut pillar portable barometer by Thomas Tompion, c. 1700 (*Christies, London*). *Fig.* 22 Japanned or lacquered pendant portable barometer. Unsigned, c. 1705 (*Gerald Campbell, Lechlade*).

24

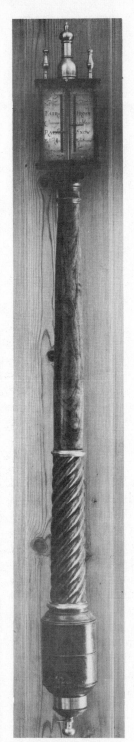

Fig. 23 Walnut pendant portable barometer. Unsigned, c. 1705 (*Mallett & Son (Antiques) Ltd, London*). *Fig.* 24 Detail of *Fig.* 23.

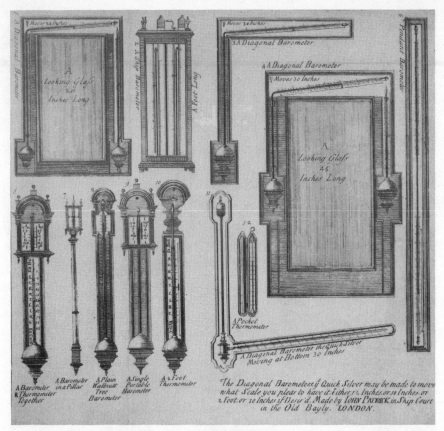

Fig. 25   Advertisement of John Patrick, c. 1710 (*Trustees of the British Museum*).

because it was designed only to hang on a wall. The one shown in *Fig.* 18 has an ivory case with silvered register plates with words as those shown in *Fig.* 16. The borders, sides and hood are engraved with chevron and scrolling foliage, and gilt brass rings support the ivory pillar sections. The cistern nut is brass and the height is 37 inches. It is numbered '64'.

A very similar barometer is illustrated in *Fig.* 19. It was made by Quare but on the hood is engraved 'Repaired by John Stenson, Derby'. He was a barometer-maker and published a pamphlet in 1782 headed 'Observations on the Barometer' which he gave to purchasers of barometers.

Fig. 21 shows one of the few pillar walnut barometers made by Thomas Tompion around 1700. The weather indications are similar to those used by Quare and the register plates are enclosed in a rectangular case, with metal-gilt borders engraved with a mask and scrolling foliage, inscribed along the base 'Thos. Tompion, Londini, Fecit'. The case has a plain turned and spirally turned column on a square plinth with four metal-gilt adjustable splayed feet which are decorated with winged cupids' masks with foliage sprays in relief. It is 37½ inches high.

Tompion (1638–1713) was the son of a Bedfordshire blacksmith and is

26

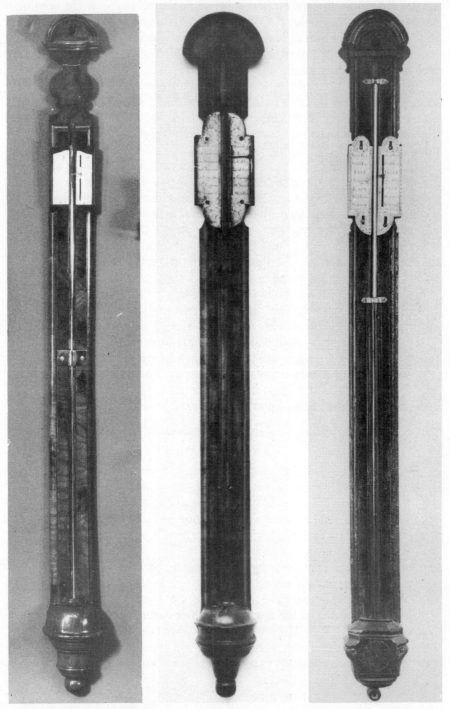

Fig. 26 Plain walnut cistern barometer. Unsigned, c. 1710 (*Sotheby's, London*).   *Fig.* 27 Plain walnut cistern barometer. Unsigned, c. 1710 (*Mallett & Son (Antiques) Ltd, London*).   *Fig.* 28 Plain walnut open cistern country barometer. Unsigned, c. 1710.

acknowledged as the most famous of English clockmakers. He became a Master of the Clockmakers' Company in 1704 and was not only 'a person justly famous for his excellent skill in making watches and clocks' but also 'not less curious and dexterous in the construction and handworking of other nice mechanick instruments'.

Figs. 23 and 24 show an unsigned walnut Quare-type barometer with summer and winter weather indications similar to those on the register plates of the open cistern barometer already discussed. The engraved foliate decoration is not seen on Quare plates which suggests it was not made by him.

The best pictorial evidence of the barometers that were made for sale to the public early in the eighteenth century can be seen in John Patrick's advertisement of around 1710 (*Fig.* 25). The various barometers shown will be discussed in later chapters dealing with these particular types. Note that they all have portable screws. The 'Barometer in a Pillar', numbered 7 in the advertisement, is very similar to the barometers made by Quare, particularly the one illustrated in *Fig.* 20. Barometers of this type survive that are signed by Patrick and, no doubt, he made many of those that are unsigned.

Fig. 26 shows a plain walnut cistern barometer similar to number 8 of Patrick's advertisement. The shaped silvered register plates have summer and winter weather indications and are engraved with leaves and flowers. The moulded case has an arched cresting and turned cistern cover with the tube protected by a walnut sheath. There is a hanging hole in the hood.

A country-made plain solid walnut open cistern barometer is illustrated in *Fig.* 28. The reservoir in this case is a porcelain pot, rather than the usual glass bowl, and the register plates are adjustable.

28

3

Early Georgian, 1714–60

From this period most cistern barometers were fitted with some sort of device which made them reasonably portable, and improvements continued to be made. It was found that boxwood was pervious to air and suitable to form a closed cistern. The top of a hollow cylinder of boxwood was cemented to within an inch of the bottom of the tube, whilst the bottom of the cylinder was covered by a shallow leather bag which, again, rested on a padded adjustable screw. By adjusting the screw, the barometer could be set at the correct reading by comparison with other barometers; it could also be made portable by the action of the screw raising the leather base until the cistern and tube were full of mercury. *Fig.* 29 shows a portable boxwood cistern tube.

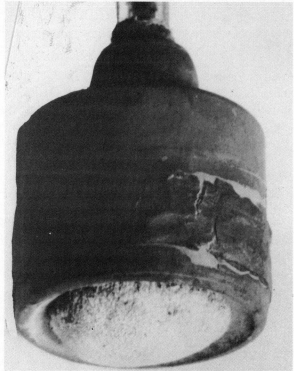

Fig. 29   Portable boxwood cistern tube.

The demand for domestic barometers grew rapidly at the beginning of the eighteenth century and they were made increasingly by mathematical, optical and philosophical instrument-makers as well as clockmakers, but it was the latter who made the more attractive barometers by producing them in ornamental and embellished cases.

Richard Neve commented in his *Baroscopologia* in 1708:

The baroscope is an instrument well known to most men; few gentlemen being without one of them, though few of them understand its right management and use . . . the tube is set in a curious frame of wood; that is as well ornamental as useful . . . it is needless to give any particular directions for the making of this particular instrument since any one may be easily furnished with it in London at a cheaper rate than he can make it himself.

Neve was at pains to emphasise that the barometer was an indicator rather than a forecaster of weather and gave advice on how to read it. However, he added sixteen 'Natural Predictions of Fine and Foul Weather' and reiterated that the movement of the mercury in the barometer should be considered in conjunction with such known indications. Two of these were:

Hoggs crying in an unusual manner and running unquietly up and down, with litter in their mouths, foreshews Rain and Storms at hand.

If crows caw and cry early in the morning, with a loud clear voice, it shews that the day will be fair.

An ornamental barometer in a curious frame of oak is shown in *Fig.* 30. It is in the manner of John Patrick's barometer numbered 6 in his advertisement, but profusely decorated in gilt in the chinoiserie style over a marbled ground. The architectural pediment is supported on Tuscan columns and surmounted by gilded brass sphere finials. The engraved silvered brass register plates have the usual wheat-ear border decoration and summer and winter weather indications identical to those on the detail in *Fig.* 32. A sealed alcohol thermometer is fitted with a paper scale which extends to the full length of the trunk; it is known as the Royal Society scale and is calibrated from 0° 'Extream Hott' down to 90° 'Extream Cold', the opposite to that expected. The bulb of the thermometer is housed within the cistern cover so that it can accurately record the temperature of the mercury. This type of thermometer appears to have been used on barometers during the first quarter of the eighteenth century.

To allow the thermometer to be attached to the front of the case the barometer is fitted with a bayonet-type tube; by bending or crimping the tube just below the register plates it allows the lower part of the tube to be enclosed within the panelled case. This type of tube was used whenever the maker wished to incorporate a thermometer directly on to a barometer case.

Figs. 31 and 32 illustrate a similar barometer made around 1720 in an oak

30

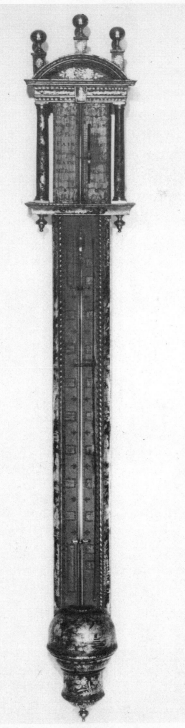

case veneered with walnut. The shaped and moulded cresting is surmounted by three ball finials gilded on gesso, as are the bases and capitals to the side pillars and the drop finials. The detail photograph (*Fig.* 32) shows the decoration of the register plates and Royal Society thermometer scale. The barometer is unsigned but the maker used some paper as packing for the tube inside the cistern cover. It was half of an advertisement by Stephen Davenport, over against the Distillery, High Holborn, near Drury Lane. He was a mathematical instrument-maker and the advertisement includes the following:

Wind guns made musquet fashion, but much neater, being discharged by the force of injected air, and will do the same execution (at a considerable distance) as if loaded with gunpowder.

The machine and glasses for the new way of cupping without fire: also lamps and glasses for cupping with fire.

Scarificators, which at once make ten, thirteen, or sixteen incisions.

Blow pipes, with or without valves: also embies and turnagates for surgeons.

Weather glasses of all sorts, viz. portable, diagonal, horizontal, wheel and marine barometers; which shew the various alterations in the weight of the air, and foretel the changes of weather consequent thereon: also thermometers, accurately adjusted, whereby the different degrees of heat and cold residing in the air at different times.

Fig. 30 Decorated oak cistern barometer. Unsigned, c. 1720 (*Phillips, London*).

31

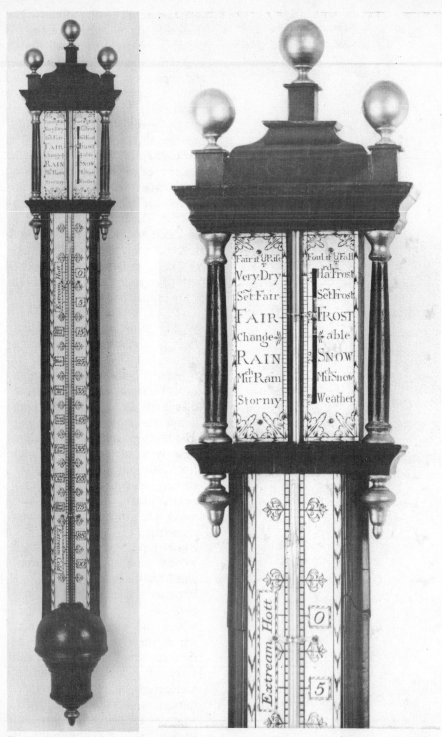

Fig. 31 Walnut cistern barometer with Royal Society scale thermometer. Unsigned, but probably by Stephen Davenport, c. 1720. *Fig.* 32 Detail of *Fig.* 31.

32

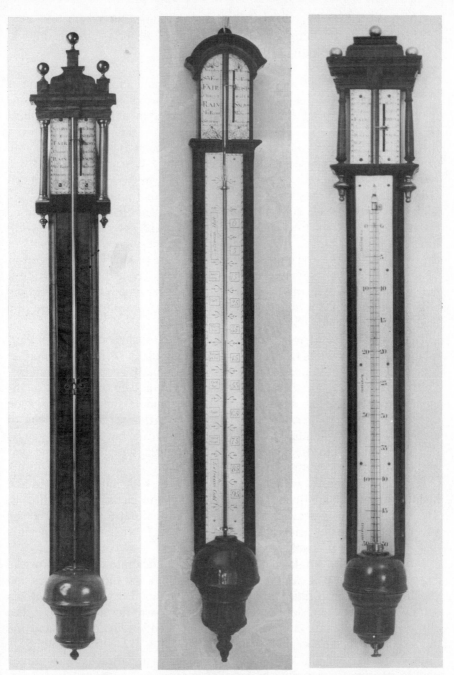

Fig. 33 Walnut cistern barometer in moulded case and turned cistern cover. Silvered brass register plates with scroll decoration, 41 inches high. Unsigned, c. 1720 (*Sotheby's, London*).   *Fig.* 34 Walnut cistern barometer in moulded case with domed hood. Silvered brass register plates and Royal Society thermometer with silvered scales. Unsigned, c. 1720 (*H. W. Keil Ltd, Broadway*).   *Fig.* 35 Walnut cistern barometer in moulded case and turned cistern cover. Silvered brass register plates with summer and winter weather indications. Royal Society thermometer with silvered scale from 0° 'Extreme Hot' to 50° 'Just Freez'. Unsigned, c. 1720 (*Park Street Antiques, Berkhamstead*).

33

Machines for shewing the use of all the mechanical powers.
Mouth-pieces for trumpets and french-horns of all sorts, either in brass
or silver, made exactly to fit any lip.

Davenport flourished between 1720 and 1737 and almost certainly made
this barometer; from his advertisement it is clear that he made the same
types of barometer produced by John Patrick and shown in his advertisement
(*Fig. 25*).

A very similar portable cistern walnut barometer is shown in *Fig.* 36,
except that it is fitted with a thermometer with a Fahrenheit scale. It was
made around 1724 which was the year in which G. D. Fahrenheit
(1686–1736), a German scientist, devised a thermometer scale which
achieved widespread acclaim and was adopted in English-speaking
countries. He used the freezing and boiling points of water as fixed temperatures and divided the interval between these temperatures into 180 parts or
degrees. Finding that the temperature of a mixture of salt, water and ice was
32 of these degrees below the freezing point of water, he called this the zero
temperature. The freezing point of water then became 32 and the boiling
point 212. He added a fourth point, the mouth or armpit temperature of a
healthy person, which was 98.

The Fahrenheit thermometer replaced the Royal Society scale thermometer on barometers from around 1725. Fahrenheit favoured mercury as
a thermometric substance but it was only gradually adopted in England.
Spirit of wine was more frequently used, even as late as the end of the
eighteenth century, as it was easier to use and less costly. The main
drawback was that thermometers containing different concentrations of
alcohol did not give similar readings for the same scale, but an advantage was
that it expanded more extensively than mercury, when heated, and was
preferred for large thermometers.

Fig. 37 illustrates a walnut cistern barometer with moulded edges and
hood, above which are finials and a drop finial below an unbroken pediment.
The whole case is extravagantly decorated with floral marquetry and the
silvered brass register plates are decorated with leaf forms. The barometer is
unsigned but was probably made around 1730.

A barometer of a similar date, but in a more elaborate case, is shown in
Fig. 38. It has an oak case veneered with walnut and the pillar bases and
capitals and the drop finials are gilt wood. The hood, round pediment and
scrollwork above the cistern cover are decorated with floral marquetry. The
barometer scales have summer and winter weather indications and the
thermometer has a Fahrenheit scale with 'Freezing' 32°, 'Temperate' 55°,
'Summer Heat' 75° and 'Sultry' 85°. Both scales are attractively engraved
with leaves and flowers with wheat-ear borders.

Not all the barometers made around this period were of the quality of those
already described, and it appears that a large number of inferior specimens
were made by entrepreneurs who exploited the quickly expanding market in
domestic weather-glasses at this time. It was considered a necessity by
people of even moderate means to own one and this prompted Edward Saul

34

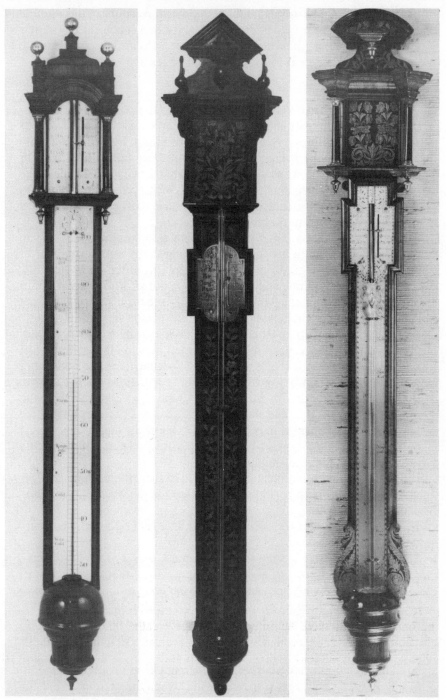

Fig. 36 Walnut cistern barometer in moulded case with silvered brass Fahrenheit scale. Unsigned, c. 1725 (*Park Street Antiques, Berkhamstead*).   *Fig.* 37 Walnut cistern barometer with floral marquetry decoration and unbroken pediment. Unsigned, c. 1730 (*Bonhams, London*).   *Fig.* 38 Walnut portable cistern barometer with floral marquetry and Fahrenheit thermometer. Unsigned, c. 1730 (*Stair & Co. Ltd, London*).

in 1735 to write 'An Historical and Philosophical Account of the Barometer or Weather-Glass'. He was Rector of Harlaxton, Lincolnshire, but it was written partly when he lived at Belvoir as tutor to John, Duke of Rutland, to whom it was dedicated. It ran to a hundred pages and included:

My Lord,

The following tract your Grace is entituled to upon many accounts. It was drawn up in part above twenty years ago, and designed for your amusement in philosophy, when I had the honour of living in the family with you in Belvoir; it has, at several times been talked over to your Grace in conversation, as occasions offered: It was some time since presented to you in manuscript, and now, with such farther additions and alterations, as, a careful review, I found reason to make, waits upon your Grace from the press . . .

The Weather-Glass being of late grown into common use, and in most houses of figure and distinction, hang up as a philosophical or ornamental branch of furniture; and supplying often matter of discourse upon the various and sudden changes of it: It may not perhaps be unacceptable to many persons, who daily see the effect, and are not rightly apprized of the cause, to explain the reason of it.

My design therefore in these papers, is not to write for the entertainment of philosophers, or of those gentlemen, who by the advantage of a learned education, or of a course of experiments, have had better opportunities of improving themselves in speculations of this nature: But for the satisfaction of many of my inquisitive countrymen; who have given themselves and their parlours an air of philosophy, by the purchase of a barometer, may be willing to know the meaning of it, and desirous of exerting now and then a superiority of understanding, by talking clearly and intelligibly upon it.

The design and use of this instrument is to shew the various changes in the weight or pressure of the air, and those of the weather depending upon it . . .
1. That in calm weather, when the air is inclined to rain, the mercury is commonly low.
2. That it is generally high in good, serene, settled, fair weather.
3. That it sinks lowest of all on very great winds, though they are not accompanied with rain; according to the point of the compass from whence they blow.
4. That, ceteris paribus, the greatest height of the mercury is found, when an easterly, or north-easterly wind blows; if it is not too strong.
5. That in calm frosty weather, the mercury is generally high.
6. That after very great storms of wind, when the mercury has been low, it usually rises very fast . . .

As for such weather-glasses, as have been lately hawked about the country, by needy foreigners, or peddling philosophers, it may not be improper to caution my readers, that they are, generally speaking, very great cheats and impositions upon those, who, for the sake of the meanness of the price, are persuaded to buy them: The cavity of the tube being, in many of them, scarce large enough to receive an ordinary pin: and the quantity of quicksilver being consequently too small, either to force the air out of the tube, at the first, or to be regularly affected by it afterwards, according to the difference of its gravitation.

I shall only add by way of advertisement. That it may perhaps, be an inducement to some of the gentlemen of Lincolnshire, to deal with Mr. Jonathan Sisson, mathematical instrument maker, at the corner of Beaufort Buildings, in the Strand, London; that he is their countryman, and eminent for his great skill, accuracy and fidelity, both in con-struction of his barometers and in whatever other works he undertakes, or delivers out of his hands.

No doubt these particular makers used tubes and cisterns of small diameter to save mercury, which caused the readings to be inaccurate and fitted them in plain cases to save expense; it is therefore not surprising that none appears to have survived.

Jonathan Sisson (1690–1747) was born in Lincolnshire and had estab-lished a workshop in the Strand by 1722. He made optical and mathematical instruments of distinction, and in 1729 was appointed instrument-maker to the Prince of Wales. He was considered specially adept at the precise division of scales but very few of his instruments appear to have survived.

A barometer made around 1740 by George Adams, a very famous mathematical instrument-maker, is shown in *Fig.* 39. The moulded walnut case has an arched cresting with spirally turned columns, with Corinthian capitals, at the sides of the register plates; these are signed 'G. Adams, London' and are engraved with rococo foliage. The weather indications are limited to Fair, Variable and Rain on the left with Frost and Snow on the right, whilst the numerical scale from 28 inches to 31 inches is given on both sides.

Fig. 40 illustrates the trade card of George Adams which outlines the vast range of his instruments. The 'curious' barometers he made are covered in two lines, being diagonal, wheel, standard or portable, with or without thermometers. He was best known for his microscopes and telescopes.

Adams was apprenticed to James Parker in 1724 and then in 1726 to Thomas Heath who was a notable instrument-maker and active from 1714; he also made barometers similar to the Adams' barometer in *Fig.* 39. By 1738 Adams had set up in business at Tycho Brahe's Head, Fleet Street; he moved to 60 Fleet Street in 1757. The quality of his work was exceptional although he was one of the first to use 'mass-production' methods. He explained his responsibilities in his workshop with regard to his instruments as:

That their exactness may be particularly attended to, I always inspect and direct the several pieces myself, see them all combined in my own house, and finish the most curious parts thereof with my own hands.

He considered that:

Mathematical instruments are the means by which those noble sciences, geometry and philosophy are rendered useful in the affairs of life. By their assistance an abstracted and unprofitable speculation, is made beneficial in a thousand instances: In a word, they enable us to connect theory and practice, and so turn what was only bare contemplation into the most substancial uses.

Between 1746 and 1748 Adams was appointed instrument-maker to His Majesty's Office of Ordnance, later instrument-maker to the Prince of Wales and then to him when he became King in 1760. Adams had two sons, George and Dudley; they both became instrument-makers and successively traded from 60 Fleet Street when their father died in 1772.

The study and collecting of antique barometers would be far less interesting if the majority of makers had not signed their instruments. For this we must thank the Clockmakers' Company which, on obtaining the right to bear arms, compelled its members to sign their pieces. Forgeries were common even in the earliest days and it was because so much inferior work had been sold under the leading names, both in England and abroad, that in 1698 an Act of Parliament required every clock to be signed with the maker's 'Name and Place of Abode or Freedom'.

The majority of instrument-makers adopted the practice of

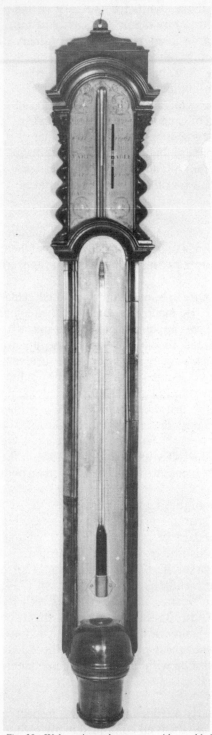

Fig. 39 Walnut cistern barometer with moulded case and arched cresting by G. Adams, London, c. 1740 (*Sotheby's, London*).

38

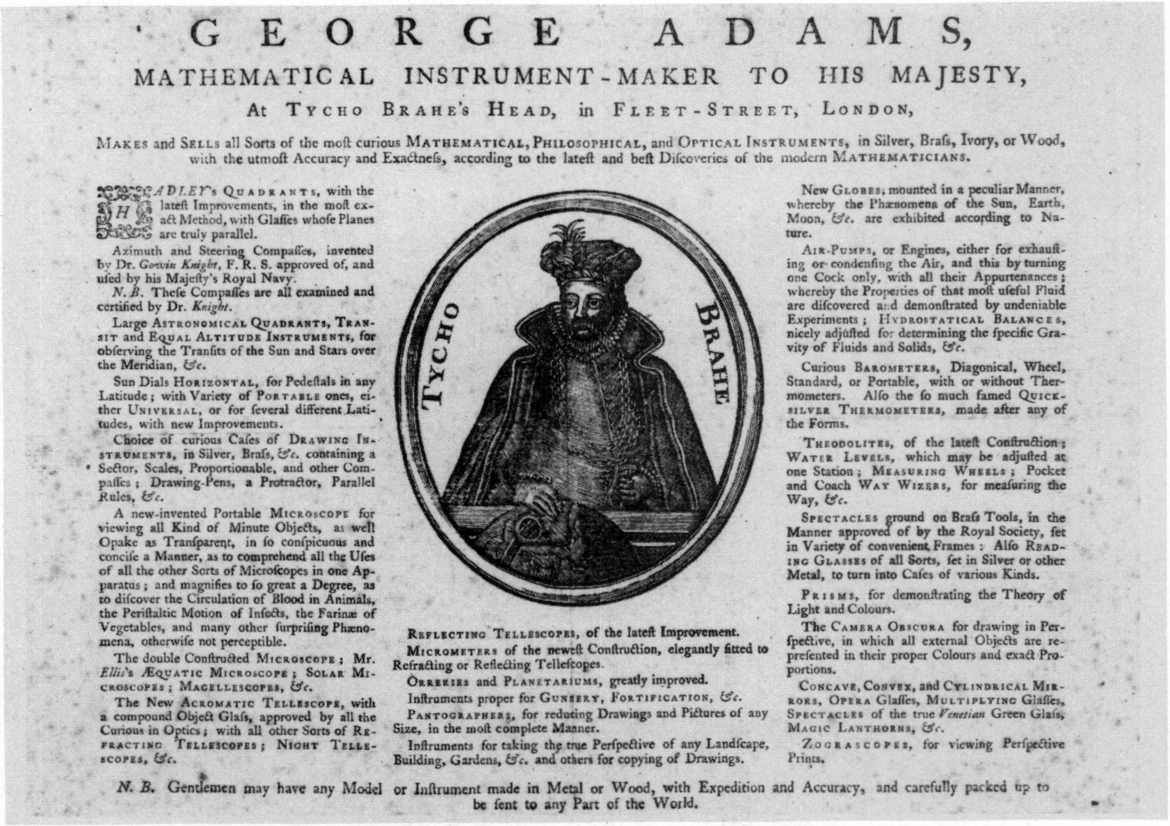

GEORGE ADAMS,

MATHEMATICAL INSTRUMENT-MAKER TO HIS MAJESTY,

At Tycho Brahe's Head, in Fleet-Street, London,

Makes and Sells all Sorts of the most curious Mathematical, Philosophical, and Optical Instruments, in Silver, Brass, Ivory, or Wood, with the utmost Accuracy and Exactness, according to the latest and best Discoveries of the modern Mathematicians.

HADLEY'S Quadrant, with the latest Improvements, in the most exact Method, with Glasses whose Planes are truly parallel.

Azimuth and Steering Compasses, invented by Dr. Gowin Knight, F. R. S. approved of, and used by his Majesty's Royal Navy.
N.B. These Compasses are all examined and certified by Dr. Knight.

Large Astronomical Quadrants, Transit and Equal Altitude Instruments, for observing the Transits of the Sun and Stars over the Meridian, &c.

Sun Dials Horizontal, for Pedestals in any Latitude; with Variety of Portable ones, either Universal, or for several different Latitudes, with new Improvements.

Choice of curious Cases of Drawing Instruments, in Silver, Brass, &c. containing a Sector, Scales, Proportionable, and other Compasses; Drawing Pens, a Protractor, Parallel Rules, &c.

A new-invented Portable Microscope for viewing all Kind of Minute Objects, as well Opake as Transparent, in so conspicuous and concise a Manner, as to comprehend all the Uses of all the other Sorts of Microscopes in one Apparatus; and magnifies to so great a Degree, as to discover the Circulation of Blood in Animals, the Peristaltic Motion of Insects, the Farina of Vegetables, and many other surprising Phenomena, otherwise not perceptible.

The double Contructed Microscope; Mr. Ellis's Aquatic Microscope; Solar Microscope; Magnifiscopes, &c.

The New Achromatic Telescope, with a compound Object Glass, approved by all the Curious in Optics; with all other Sorts of Refracting Telescopes; Night Telescopes, &c.

Reflecting Telescopes, of the newest Improvement.
Micrometers of the newest Construction, elegantly fitted to Refracting or Reflecting Telescopes.
Orreries and Planetariums, greatly improved.
Instruments proper for Gunnery, Fortification, &c.
Pantographers, for reducing Drawings and Pictures of any Size, in the most complete Manner.
Instruments for taking the true Perspective of any Landscape, Building, Gardens, &c. and others for copying of Drawings.

New Globes, mounted in a peculiar Manner, whereby the Phaenomena of the Sun, Earth, Moon, &c. are exhibited according to Nature.

Air-Pumps, or Engines, either for exhausting or condensing the Air, and this by turning one Cock only, with all their Appurtenances are discovered and demonstrated by undeniable Experiment; Hydrostatical Balances, nicely adjusted for determining the Specific Gravity of Fluids and Solids, &c.

Curious Barometers, Diagonical, Wheel, Standard, or Portable, with or without Thermometers. Also the so much famed Quick-silver Thermometers, made after any of the Form.

Theodolites, of the latest Construction; Water Levels, which may be adjusted at one Station Measuring Wheels; Pocket and Coach Way Wizers, for measuring the Way, &c.

Spectacles ground on Brass Tools, in the Manner approved of by the Royal Society, set in Variety of convenient Frames; Also Reading Glasses of all Sorts, set in Silver or other Metal, to turn into Cases of various Kinds.

Prisms, for demonstrating the Theory of Light and Colours.

The Camera Obscura for drawing in Perspective, in which all external Objects are represented in their proper Colours and exact Proportions.

Concave, Convex, and Cylindrical Mirrors, Opera Glasses, Multiplying Glasses, Spectacles of the true Venetian Green Glass, Magic Lanthorns, &c.

Zograscopes, for viewing Perspective Prints.

BRAHE

TYCHO

N.B. Gentlemen may have any Model or Instrument made in Metal or Wood, with Expedition and Accuracy, and carefully packed up to be sent to any Part of the World.

Fig. 40   Trade card of George Adams, Fleet Street, London, c. 1740 (*Science Museum, London*).

signing barometers from around 1740 and this adds greatly to their appeal, as interesting information can be obtained about the makers. The style of the signature and the engraving can be, within limits, a guide to the age of the barometer.

A workshop run by the Mann family had a long period of activity; it was started by James Mann around 1693 and he handed the business over to his son, also James Mann (c. 1685–1750), around 1717; he, in turn, was succeeded by his son John.

The address of the business was at the Sign of Sir Isaac Newton, and Two Pair of Spectacles, near the West End of St Pauls, London. James Mann junior was an optician but his trade card shows that he made numerous instruments including barometers and thermometers. It claimed to be 'The Oldest Shop'.

A walnut barometer made by him around 1740 is illustrated in *Fig.* 41. It has a moulded case and an arched cornice with a turned and spirally fluted cistern cover. The only decoration on the register plates are engraved circles round the four screws that fix them. There is a sickle-shaped recording pointer and the plates are protected by a glazed brass door.

Another important optical instrument-maker was John Cuff (1708–72). He was apprenticed to James Mann junior and called himself: 'A spectacle and microscope maker, who makes and sells, wholesale and retail, all manner of curious optical instruments'. He also made barometers and one signed 'J. Cuff. Fecit' is shown in *Fig.* 42. The panelled pine case is veneered with walnut with a distinctive turned cistern cover which only Cuff appears to have used. The moulded domed hood is surmounted by three brass finials. The silvered brass register plates, which have the usual summer weather indications, are protected by a glazed brass door.

One of the leading early eighteenth-century opticians was Edward Scarlett (1688–1743). He was apprenticed to Christopher Cock in 1691 and started on his own around 1700 at The Archimedes and Globe, Dean Street, Soho, London. His son of the same name was apprenticed to him in 1716 and their trade card, which is illustrated in *Fig.* 43, shows them to be opticians to King George II. The wording is also in French and Dutch which suggests they must have carried on a significant trade with the Continent. It is known that instruments, some made by Scarlett, were exported to America during this period. Edward Scarlett senior is associated with the popularisation of eye-glasses known as temple-spectacles because the side pieces ended in rings which pressed against the temple, rather than clipping over the ears. He died in 1743 and his son in 1779.

Fig. 44 depicts a mahogany portable cistern barometer signed 'Scarlett Fecit' at the top of the silvered brass thermometer scale. The case is solid mahogany with a turned and spirally fluted cistern cover. The mercury thermometer has a strange scale with the range: Ext. Hott 30°, Hott 20°, Warm 10°, Temp. 0°, Cold 20°, Frost 30°, Ext. Cold 40°. This does not appear to agree with any known scale used around 1740 when the barometer was made. A bayonet-type tube is used and the barometer and thermometer scales have sickle-shaped pointers, the latter slides up and down a brass rod.

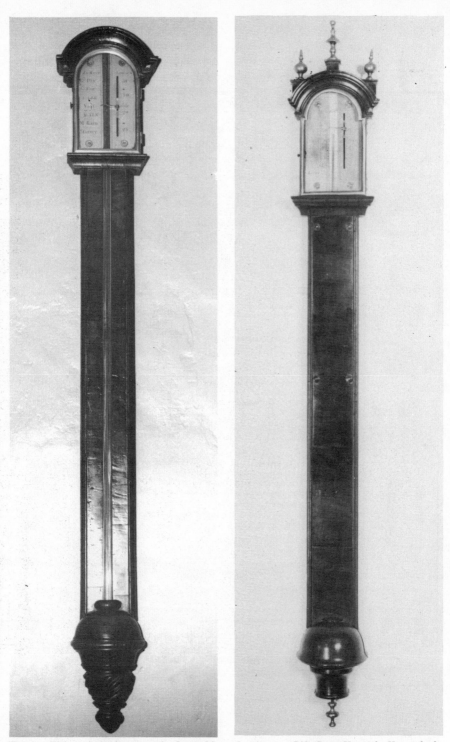

Fig. 41   Walnut cistern barometer by James Mann, London, c. 1740 (*Peter Hunwick, Hungerford*).
Fig. 42   Walnut portable barometer by J. Cuff, London, c. 1740 (*J. & M. Bristow, Tetbury*).

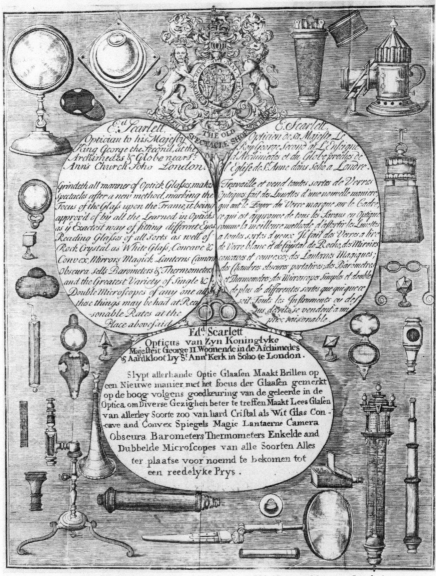

Fig. 43   Trade card of Edward Scarlett, c. 1730 (*Science Museum, London*).

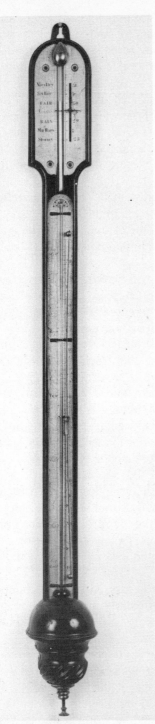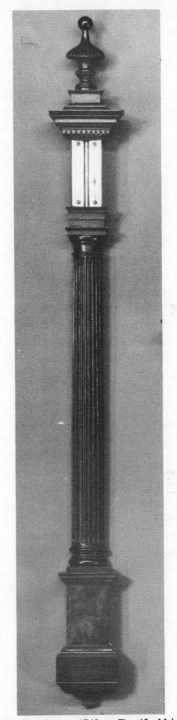

Fig. 44 Mahogany portable cistern barometer by Scarlett, London, c. 1740. *Fig.* 45 Mahogany bulb cistern barometer with Chippendale influence. Unsigned, c. 1740 (*Mallett & Son (Antiques) Ltd, London*).

Mahogany began to supersede walnut for making barometer cases during the second quarter of the eighteenth century and rapidly gained favour. Mahogany was superior to walnut in many respects, its dark reddish colour was preferred and it was found to be close grained and strong. It lasted well, did not crack or warp and was not liable to attack from woodworm.

The fashion for mahogany was encouraged in 1720 when France prohibited the export of walnut, after most of the walnut trees on the Continent had been destroyed by the severe winter of 1709. Imports of mahogany from North America and the West Indies were arranged from 1720 and this trade was substantially increased in 1733 when the duty on all imported timber was abolished.

From 1740 the frames were generally made of, or veneered with, mahogany, the designs following that of contemporary furniture, although clock-case designs were still favoured by the clockmakers. The influence of Chippendale can also be seen, with some high-quality cases lavishly carved in the rococo manner.

Fig. 45 shows a solid mahogany unsigned barometer made around 1740. It resembles the Quare-type pendant barometer and has a fluted and reeded pillar on a squared cistern cover. The dentil course set in the moulding of the cornice was certainly a Thomas Chippendale development. The enamelled register plates slope inwards and have scroll leaf decoration, with weather indications identical to those shown in *Fig.* 108. 'Inclind to Dry', 'Doubtfull' and 'Inclind to Wet' are very rarely seen.

This barometer has a bulb or bottle cistern tube (*Fig.* 46). This type of tube was being made on the Continent by 1690 but it was not popular in England and was used only rarely until the nineteenth century. The early bulb cisterns were pear-shaped with a small hole in the side to admit air; they later became more rounded, still with a hole in the side; then the bulb was left open at the top and still later a neck was added.

Its main advantage was the ease and cheapness of construction; the disadvantages were that it was not so readily portable as the cistern type and there was no successful way of determining the scale zero. The only way to adjust the height of the mercury was to raise or lower the tube or the register plates; alternatively, the level of mercury in the bulb cistern could be raised or lowered.

Dating barometers from the type of cistern used is not recommended as very often they have been replaced, particularly those from the eighteenth century. Many boxwood cistern tubes were also replaced by bulb cistern tubes because the latter were much cheaper.

The mahogany barometer in *Fig.* 47 serves to portray a Chippendale-type case. It has moulded borders with the cresting elaborately carved with satyrs' masks, shell medallions and scrolling foliage; the pediment is carved as a vase of flowers. The cistern cover is carved with drapery overlapping a scroll base and with upspringing foliage suspending floral festoons with a shell medallion. The thermometer has a Fahrenheit scale and the enamelled register plates are signed 'West, London'.

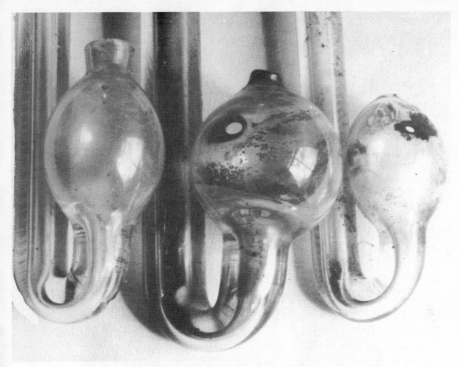

Fig. 46   Bulb or bottle cistern tubes.

By the middle of the eighteenth century an increasing number of barometers were exported and industrial methods were being used to produce them. Division of labour was in being, with glassblowers making the tubes, engravers making the register plates and cabinet-makers producing the cases; the assembly was undertaken by opticians, instrument-makers and clockmakers.

Although the vast majority of the early barometers were made in London, quite a number were produced in the country, mainly by local clockmakers. *Fig.* 48 gives an example of a country-made cistern barometer by James Verrier of North Curry in Somerset (c. 1750). He was a long-case clockmaker who appears to have developed a type of clock movement powered by barometric or temperature change. It was described in a letter to the *Western Flying Post* in 1755 as follows:

Sir,
I flatter myself the following description of a new invented clock which I have seen at North Curry made by James Verrier of that place, which will be acceptable to many of your readers if you please to give it place in your Weekly Mercury you will oblige, Sir, your constant reader.

W. B. Bridgewater 26 July

Fig. 47 Chippendale-style mahogany barometer, 60 inches high by West, London, c. 1745 (*Christies, London*). *Fig.* 48 Mahogany cistern barometer by James Verrier, North Curry, c. 1750.

Fig. 49 Detail of *Fig.* 48.

This clock I take to be the nearest to perpetual motion of anything yet discovered, as it requires no manual assistance whatever, either to wind it up or to keep it in motion, although it sometimes descends and sometimes ascends according to the different direction of the barrel, without ratchet or click, the first wheel being fixed to the barrel it shows apparent time. In this state it was first put in motion in 1752 but the inventor knowing it to be liable to the same variations which always attend clocks has endeavoured to prevent the same, which in 1754 he thus effected by being corrected to less than a minute by influence of the sun. Upon the whole it will continue to keep in motion as long as the materials will last, foulness only excepted. It is needless to mention what advantages these clocks must be to the publick, either in towns, churches or houses. The inventor on proper encouragement is willing to submit a plan of the same. The machine has had the approbation of many curious persons who have seen it.

The Verrier barometer is veneered with mahogany and has the general appearance of a long-case clock. The tube is set in a deep groove and the silvered brass register plates are protected by glass, but as there is no door the sickle-shaped set pointer is moved by a rack-and-pinion mechanism which is controlled by the key on the right-hand side of the case just below the hood. The three ball finials above the arched cornice are of brass, as are the bases and capitals of the pillars supporting the hood. The register plates are of particular interest and are shown in *Fig.* 49. The weather indications for summer and winter are given and the words are similar to those used generally up until the middle of the eighteenth century. Roman lettering with capitals and lower case is used with copperplate script. The scale is very unusual in that it only extends

Fig. 50   Mahogany bulb cistern barometer by Thomas Benbow, c. 1750.

48

from 27.7 inches to 30.4 inches whilst changeable is engraved against 29 inches; this is strange as invariably it is engraved against 29.5 inches. It could be a mistake or a possible explanation is that the barometer was made at the request of a customer who lived 500 feet or so above sea level.

Fig. 50 shows a bulb cistern barometer of the same period by Thomas Benbow. The case is of solid mahogany, as are the three ball finials. Two wire loops contain the tube and the cistern cover is held in position by pressing into the case two headless nails fixed into the cover. The register plates are of silvered brass and the summer and winter weather indications are as shown in *Fig.* 49 except that 'Stormy' and 'Tempest' are replaced by 'Tempestous'. The scale extends to 3 inches with the half-inches highlighted with large dots, but there are no numerals. The manually operated set pointer slides along a metal rod, raised above the plates, and is fixed in position by a screw.

The date the barometer was made is debatable, as unfortunately Thomas Benbow, unlike James Verrier, did not engrave his address on the plates, making it difficult to trace him. The form of engraving and weather indications used suggest that it could have been made before 1750, but the possibility is that Benbow was a country maker and copied the style at a later date. The name of the maker is below the weather indications and this suggests that it was made around the middle of the eighteenth century or earlier, when it was common practice to engrave the name in this position. Later barometers usually have the maker's name at the top of the plates.

Another noted optician who sold barometers was James Ayscough, the son of a Wiltshire clergyman. He was apprenticed to James Mann junior and started his own business in 1732 in Ludgate Street, London. In 1743 he went into partnership with Mann but they split up in 1749. One of his trade cards (*Fig.* 51) and two of his barometers are illustrated (*Figs.* 52, 53). A feature of both barometers is that they are fitted with verniers so that a more accurate reading can be taken from the scale.

Until the middle of the eighteenth century the makers satisfied themselves as to the accuracy of their barometers by ensuring that wide cisterns were used. It will be appreciated that if the diameter of the cistern is very many times greater than the bore of the tube, then the change in cistern level of the mercury will be negligible when the mercury in the tube moves between 28 and 31 inches. However, in order to take more accurate readings, a vernier was usually fitted to cistern tube barometers from around 1750.

The vernier was invented around 1630 by Pierre Vernier of Ornans in Burgundy. It can be seen in detail in *Fig.* 62. The barometer scales are usually divided into inches and tenths of an inch, whilst the vernier is one and one-tenth inches long and divided into ten equal parts numbered one to ten. The vernier scale is made to pass along the fixed barometer scale by a sliding or rack-and-pinion movement. If the first line of the vernier is in line with a one-tenth division on the scale, then the second line on the vernier will be out of line with the next one-tenth division by one-hundredth of an inch. It follows that if the first line on the vernier is out of line with any division on the scale, the correct reading can be obtained by seeing which vernier line

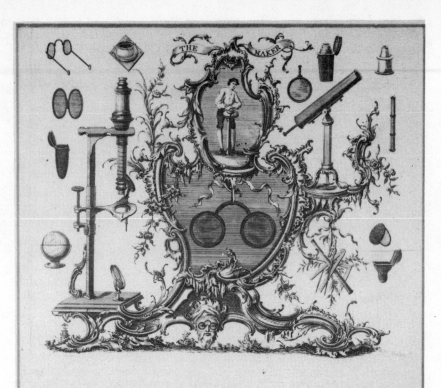

J A M E S   A Y S C O U G H,

O P T I C I A N,

At the Great GOLDEN SPECTACLES, in *Ludgate-Street*, near St. PAUL's, *LONDON*,

(*Removed from Sir* ISAAC NEWTON's HEAD *in the same Street*)

 AKES and SELLS, (Wholesale and Retail) SPECTACLES and READING-GLASSES, either of *Brazil*-Pebbles, White, Green, or Blue Glass, ground after the truest Method, set in neat and commodious Frames.

CONCAVES for SHORT-SIGHTED PERSONS.

REFLECTING and REFRACTING TELESCOPES of various Lengths, (some of which are peculiarly adapted to use at Sea;) Double and Single MICROSCOPES, with the latest Improvements; PRISMS; CAMERA OBSCURA's; Concave and Convex SPECULUMS; MAGICK LANTHORNS; OPERA GLASSES; BAROMETERS and THERMOMETERS; SPEAKING and HEARING-TRUMPETS; with all other Sorts of Optical, as well as Mathematical and Philosophical Instruments.

Together with Variety of MAPS, and GLOBES of all Sizes.

Fig. 51   Trade card of James Ayscough, c. 1750 (*Science Museum, London*).

coincides with a division on the scale. By setting the vernier zero pointer to the level of the mercury and reading the scale in conjunction with the vernier scale, an accuracy of up to one-hundredth of an inch can be achieved.

Fig. 52 depicts a plain red walnut barometer with a rounded top and hemispherical cistern cover by James Ayscough, whilst *Fig.* 53 portrays a very decorative mahogany barometer also by him. A mirror is mounted on a mahogany base to form a panel over which is elaborate carving in mahogany of foliage, flowers and fruit using scroll patterns. The cistern cover is in the form of a carved and gilded face representing the sun. The barometer and thermometer scales are of silvered brass protected by glass and the vernier is adjusted by a screw at the right-hand side of the case.

The work of John Bird (1709—76) had a profound influence on the middle decades of the eighteenth century. He was an optical and mathematical instrument-maker in Durham until he moved to London in 1740 and worked for George Graham (1673—1751) and Jonathan Sisson (1690—1747). It is not known exactly when he acquired his own workshop in the Strand, but by 1744 he had made a barometer for the Meteorological Station of Roger Pickering, who described it as follows:

I have found those with open cisterns more sensible than the portable ones. That with which I make my observations, is with an open cistern, furnished with micrometer [vernier] that divides an inch into 400 parts; by which I am capable of perceiving the most minute alteration of the gravity of the air; it was made by Mr. Bird of the Strand, whose accuracy in graduation deserves, I think, notice and encouragement.

John Bird was a well-known maker of barometers, thermometers and astronomical instruments and was renowned for his accurate scales. In 1767 he published his method of dividing astronomical instruments and he improved the vernier by developing a tangent screw, which was a slow-motion precision screw for fine adjustment.

One of his open cistern barometers is shown in *Figs.* 54 and 55. The case is of oak veneered with mahogany whilst the cistern cover, ball finials and part of the hood are of solid walnut. The overall height is 44 inches, whilst the hemispherical cistern cover has a width of 5 inches and is more than 3 inches in depth. The vernier is operated manually within a groove on the register plates; these have weather indications which became standard around this time and have been used ever since.

The tube is of particular interest as it was widened to a bulb at the top with a diameter of approximately 2 inches. The bulb, protected by a brass cap, was designed to dilute the effect of any air or vapour that might, in time, percolate into the vacuum. This type of tube was also used by John Bennett, Jesse Ramsden, John Troughton, Edward Nairne and Jeremiah Sisson. A barometer by Sisson is illustrated in *Fig.* 56. The frame is of solid mahogany and the top half of the cistern cover can be lifted off to see the level of the mercury in the iron open cistern, which has a diameter of 4¾ inches. A fixed ivory scale is attached to the frame just above the cistern; it has an ivory

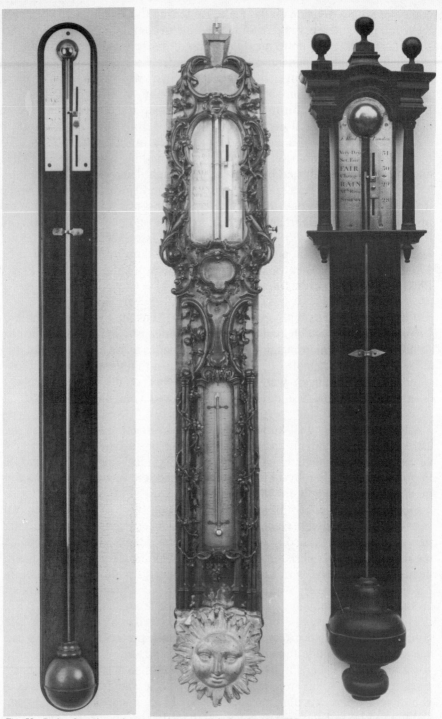

Fig. 52   Red walnut cistern barometer by Ayscough, London, c. 1755.   *Fig.* 53   Mahogany portable cistern barometer by J. Ayscough, London, c. 1755 (Crown Copyright, *Victoria and Albert Museum, London*).   *Fig.* 54   Mahogany and walnut open cistern barometer by J. Bird, London, c. 1760.

Fig. 55   Detail of *Fig.* 54.

53

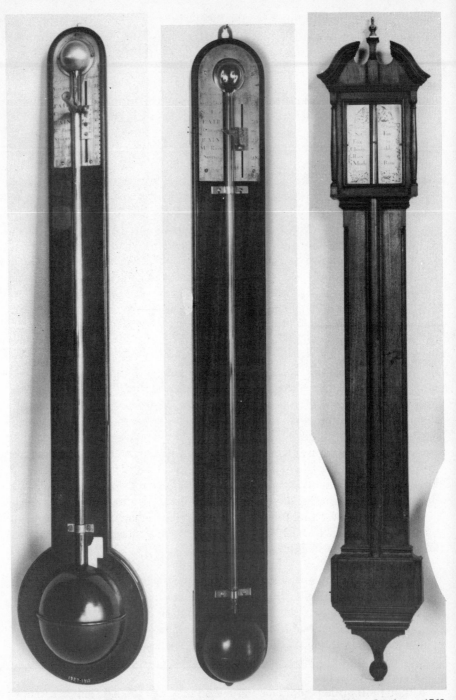

Fig. 56 Open cistern mahogany barometer with vernier and microscope by J. Sisson, London, c. 1760 (*Science Museum, London*).   *Fig.* 57 Open cistern mahogany barometer by Ramsden, London, c. 1770 (British Crown Copyright, *Science Museum, London*).   *Fig.* 58 Bulb cistern mahogany barometer with broken arched pediment, brass urn finial and silvered brass register plates. Unsigned, c. 1760 (*Lalonde Bros. & Parham, Bristol*).

vernier which can be adjusted to the level of the mercury in the cistern and this allows corrections to be applied to the reading of the mercury in the tube. The barometer has a vernier 1.6 inches long and calibrated from 0 to 50, also a low-power microscope, adjustable for height, to focus on the mercury meniscus in the tube.

This type of barometer could be classed as a scientific instrument as they were not made for sale to the general public; they appear to have been produced for scientists who took an interest in recording meteorological phenomena and required a very accurate instrument.

Jeremiah Sisson succeeded his father Jonathan Sisson in 1747 and was active until at least 1788 when he was instrument-maker to the Prince of Wales. He was a mathematical instrument-maker and at least maintained the eminence of his father.

A similar open cistern barometer with a large bulb at the top of the tube and a fixed ivory pointer, to allow zero shift correction, is illustrated in *Fig.* 57. It has a solid mahogany case, with moulded edges, and the top half of the hemispherical cistern cover can be removed to view the mercury level. The silvered brass register plates have an unusual vernier as there are two connected pointers; one goes behind the tube and the other, which is in front of the tube, is hinged and has a notch at the centre of the tube so that readings can be taken at the middle of the meniscus.

According to George Adams junior, this improvement of the indexes was one, among many, for which science was indebted to Jesse Ramsden, who made the barometer around 1770. Ramsden was probably the greatest instrument-maker of all time. He was born in Halifax in 1735, the son of a linen draper, and worked for his father for a time, but by 1758 he was apprenticed to an optician in London. He made instruments for Jonathan Sisson, George Adams, George Dolland and Edward Nairne before setting up in business in the Haymarket around 1768. His trade card shows him to have been a mathematical, optical and philosophical instrument-maker near the Little Theatre in the Haymarket, St James's.

The scientific literature towards the end of the eighteenth century was full of his praise. In 1787 J. D. Cassini, who bought instruments for the Paris Observatory, wrote of Ramsden:

I have been able to give you a very inadequate picture of the admiration which the sight of the splendid instruments made in England by the famous Ramsden roused in us. The richness of this artist's creative genius, the perfection of his execution, and his wide experience, force me to recognize that it will be a long time before anyone will be able, I do not say to surpass, but even to equal his achievement.

Although Ramsden employed more than fifty workmen he appears to have undertaken himself the construction of the most delicate instruments. He had only just retired when he died in 1800.

A barometer made by a clockmaker is shown in *Figs.* 59 and 60. He was John Rittson from Tekrill, Nr Reeth, North Yorkshire, who was active

Fig. 59   Portable cistern barometer in padouk wood by J. Rittson, c. 1760.   *Fig.* 60   Detail of *Fig.* 59.

56

Fig. 61 Trade card of Benjamin Martin, c. 1760 (*Science Museum, London*).

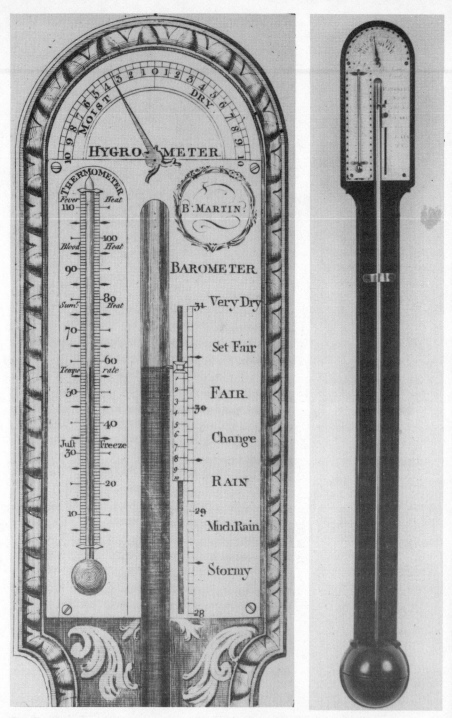

Fig. 62 Illustration of an 'Aerometrum Magnum or The Triple Weather Glass' from his *General Magazine of the Arts and Sciences* by Benjamin Martin, 1759 (*The British Library*).   Fig. 63 Mahogany triple weather-glass by B. Martin, London, c. 1760.

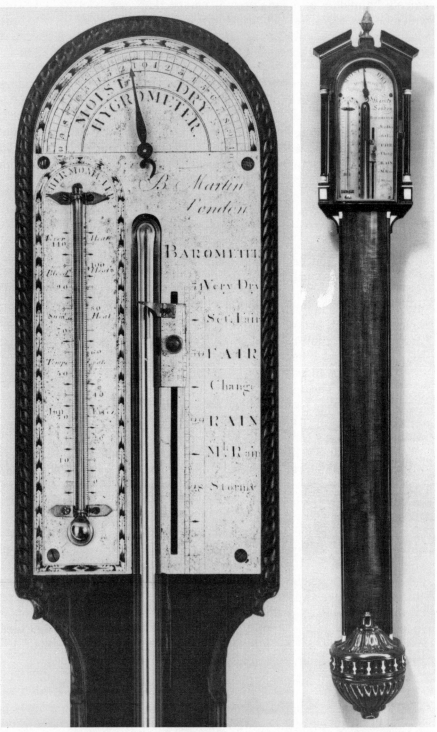

Fig. 64 Detail of Fig. 63.   Fig. 65 Mahogany cistern barometer by Martin, London, c. 1760
(Hotspur Ltd, London).

around the middle of the eighteenth century. The case is of padouk wood with moulded edges and an unusual turned cistern cover. The silvered brass register plates are headed 'The Great Barometer' which was a feature of Rittson's barometers although it is only the usual size with an overall height of 37 inches.

The cornice is in the form of a broken pediment which became popular on barometers from about 1760 right up until 1840. This type of pediment had been surmounting the cornices of bookcases and cabinets since 1715.

An important barometer-maker who made distinctive instruments was Benjamin Martin (1704–82) and his trade card is reproduced in *Fig.* 61. He was born in Worplesdon, Surrey and was a teacher before moving to London in 1740 to work as an assistant to the scientist, J. T. Desaguliers. Whilst a teacher, he made microscopes and other optical instruments and appears to have set up in business in Fleet Street in 1744.

He was an enterprising instrument-maker who lectured and wrote copiously about his instruments; his shop was one of the best equipped and he held courses and public demonstrations which were well attended. He wrote over thirty popular scientific works and in 1755 launched a monthly *General Magazine of the Arts and Sciences* which ran until 1765. These were subsequently published in book form and *Fig.* 62 shows an illustration of a triple weather-glass taken from it. It is almost identical to the mahogany barometer by B. Martin, London, portrayed in *Figs.* 63 and 64 and proves that he used his own instruments as illustrations for his writings.

The case has moulded edges with carved gadrooning decoration round the register plates. The top half of the hemispherical cistern cover can be removed to view the fixed boxwood gauge, which indicates the correct level of mercury in the open cistern. The weather and temperature indications are identical and on a silvered brass plate.

This barometer is called a triple weather-glass because it has three aids to weather forecasting: a barometer, thermometer and hygrometer. The hygrometer, or hygroscope as it was also known, is used to determine the humidity of the air. The barometer reading is affected by a change in wind velocity as well as by rain and one objection raised against the simple barometer was that the owner was in doubt, when the mercury level was falling, whether to expect rain or wind. The addition of a hygrometer, indicating the degree of dampness or dryness of the air, removed this doubt.

A barometer belonging to King George II (1727–60) once indicated on a silvered scale the words 'Rising-Dry, Serene'. Unfortunately, it was blowing a gale outside and the notoriously bad-tempered King threw it out of the window exclaiming 'See for yourself'. Even today many people expect from a barometer the accuracy of a clock, forgetting that weather also depends on temperature, altitude, wind direction and humidity.

Robert Hooke appears to have made the first hygrometer in England. On 7 December 1663 he read a paper to the Royal Society on his 'Weather Observations' which included the following: 'For ascertaining . . . the moisture and dryness of the air with the degree of it . . . this is to be observed with a good hygroscope, which may be had either with the beard of an oat,

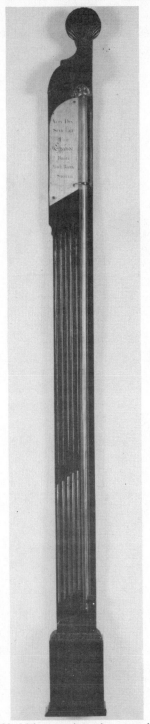

a gut string or the like.' In June 1666 he recommended the 'cod of a vetch' as a substitute for a single beard of wild oat. Other materials used were hair, sheep gut or fiddle strings, whalebone and hatters' paper.

Benjamin Martin appears to have been one of the first to add hygrometers to his barometers as they began to appear on some instruments from around 1760. He was almost alone in preferring the gut type, the mechanism of which is behind the register plates. The arbor of the indicating pointer is fixed to a cog which is moved by a rack and wheel. One end of the catgut is wound round and fixed to the wheel whilst the other end is anchored to the case. The rack is held under tension by a spring so that the expansion and contraction of the gut is conveyed to the indicating pointer.

Fig. 65 illustrates a far more elaborate barometer by Martin. The case is veneered with mahogany and the trunk is of serpentine section. Ivory is used as decoration for the bases and capitals of the side pillars and the moulding below the hood. The cistern cover is decorated with gadrooning and a spindle gallery made of ivory and ebonised wood spindles used alternatively. The silvered brass register plates are protected by a glazed brass door.

Fig. 66 shows a rare asymmetric mahogany cistern barometer. It has an elegantly fluted trunk with brass fillets on the lower section and a scallop shell decorates the pediment. The brass register plates are silvered and the gilt metal pierced guard to the tube is inscribed

'Tarts, London' and numbered '600'. The name Tarts is not recorded as a barometer-maker by G. H. Baillie who notes that this name appeared on many watches made for the Dutch market and is probably fictitious.

4

Late Eighteenth Century, 1760–1800

It was during the first twenty years or so following the accession of George III in 1760 that the London instrument-makers rose to the height of their fame on the Continent. Every European observatory prided itself on the possession of instruments by Bird, Sisson, Dolland, Adams, Nairne, Ramsden and other Englishmen. This supremacy may well have been occasioned by social conditions. In England there was a free and friendly social intercourse between scientists and technicians which was out of the question in the more rigidly graded societies of France and Germany where the craftsman so clearly belonged to a lower rank than the scientist.

Late eighteenth-century barometers tended to be plainer, except for those specially made to an individual customer's requirements, with less decoration to the frame; the engraving on the register plates and thermometer scales was less ornamental and these trends were brought about to standardise the component parts for reasons of economy. The trunk of the barometer became narrower and the influence of the long-case clock design disappeared.

When mahogany was first used for barometer cases around 1740 the solid wood was used without veneer, as it was considered that its colour and grain were sufficiently attractive. However, over the following twenty years some makers applied a mahogany veneer to the mahogany frame, and after 1760 very few barometers were made without some kind of veneer.

Fig. 67 shows a plain portable cistern barometer made around 1765. The frame is of mahogany with a mahogany veneer across the front of the case, bordered by an eighth of an inch mahogany stringing round the frame. The maker was George Burton of 136 High Street, Borough, Southwark, London, who was an instrument-maker and active for the next fifty years. His instruments were taken on Captain James Cook's Second Voyage of Discovery in 1772. They comprised 'Two Portable barometers, six thermometers, a theodolite, level and Gunter's chain'. He was paid £79 13s for them by the Navy Board. William Gooch also took a portable barometer by Burton on his voyage to South America in 1792.

A unique cistern barometer is illustrated in *Fig.* 68 profusely decorated with ormolu mounts. The silvered register plates, which have two pointers, are contained in a cartouche with a sunburst mask cresting, shells at the side and a batwinged devil's head below. The thermometer scales are surmounted by a shell and flanked by chains of fruit, holly and bay above acanthus

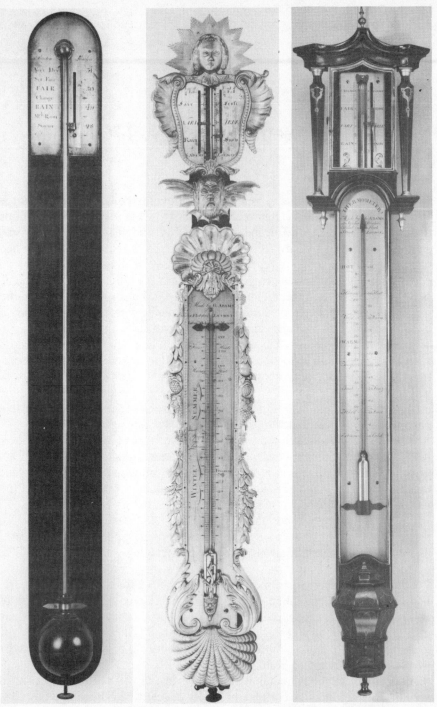

Fig. 67 Mahogany cistern barometer by Burton, London, c. 1765. *Fig.* 68 Ormolu cistern barometer by G. Adams, Fleet Street, London, c. 1765 (*Sotheby's, London*). *Fig.* 69 Mahogany cistern barometer by G. Adams at Tycho Brahe's Head in Fleet Street, London, c. 1770 (*Hotspur Ltd, London*).

scrolls. The cistern cover is adorned with a reversed scallop shell. In addition to the usual temperature wording, the Fahrenheit thermometer scale has Summer, Spring and Autumn, and Winter calibrations, with Spring and Autumn limited to between 45 and 55 degrees.

The barometer and thermometer scales are both signed, with more detail on the thermometer which reads: 'Made by G. Adams in Fleet Street, London, Instrument Maker to His Majesty'. This is the George Adams (1704–72) mentioned in chapter 3, who was the most prominent name associated with the royal 'Philosophical Cabinet', a collection of some 350 items collected by George III, many of which were specially made for the collection.

Another barometer by G. Adams is shown in *Fig.* 69. The frame is made of mahogany with brass decoration on the cistern cover and on the tapered hexagonal pillars to the hood. Brass is also used for the glazed door protecting the register plates and on the thermometer scale bezel. The vernier can be adjusted by the hinged rod which hangs from it.

The barometer is signed 'G. Adams, London' whilst the thermometer is annotated 'Made by G. Adams at Tycho Brahe's Head in Fleet Street, London'. It could have been made by George Adams, the maker of the barometers in *Figs.* 39 and 68, or by his son George Adams (1750–95), who succeeded to the business on his father's death in 1772. He was apprenticed to his father in 1765 and took over the appointment of instrument-maker to George III; later he became optician to the Prince of Wales. The quality of his instruments was at least as good as those of his father and he wrote various essays and dissertations on instruments, including one on barometers, thermometers and other meteorological instruments in 1790 which will be discussed below.

The most common type of barometer made around 1765 is illustrated in *Fig.* 70. The case has a pine base with moulded mahogany sides and solid mahogany broken pediment and cistern cover. The front of the case is veneered with mahogany and the adjustable cistern screw shape is typical of the period. In design this barometer is much narrower and generally more slender than earlier barometers and for this reason the type became known as a stick barometer.

An interesting cistern barometer in a mahogany case is shown in *Fig.* 71. It was made around 1770 by Dollond, London, and has an unusual round cistern cover which was occasionally used on barometers by George Adams and Jesse Ramsden. It also has a rare type of hygrometer, recommended by J. A. De Luc, which uses a whalebone attached to the top of the dial pillar; the scale is calibrated from 0 to 110.

The Fahrenheit thermometer is also unusual in that it has a correction scale. No adjustment is needed at $55°$ but the instruction is to add $5/100$ inch to the barometer reading at $40°$ and $1/10$ inch at $24°$; conversely, $5/100$ inch is to be subtracted at $70°$, $1/10$ inch at $86°$ and $15/1000$ inch at $102°$. Mercury, being a liquid, is more expansible by heat than either glass or the scale; consequently, the level of the barometer will rise with any rise in temperature and fall with a fall in temperature even though the air pressure remains constant.

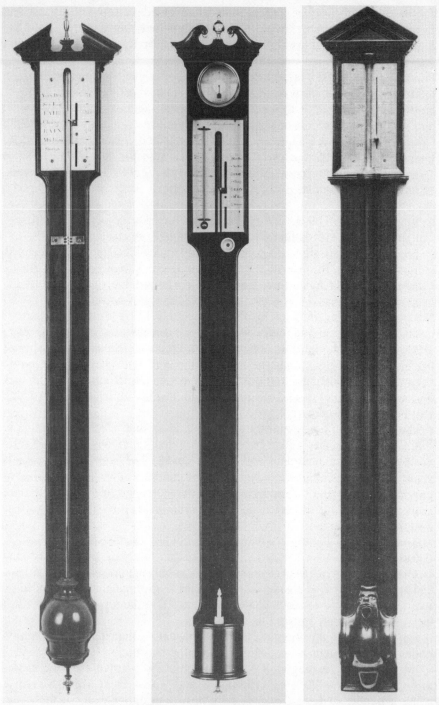

Fig. 70 Mahogany cistern barometer. Unsigned, c. 1765. *Fig.* 71 Mahogany cistern barometer with hygrometer and ivory float by Dollond, London, c. 1770. *Fig.* 72 Mahogany bulb cistern barometer with triangular pediment and cistern cover carved as a grotesque bearded mask, 39 inches high. Unsigned, c. 1770 (*Christies, London*).

The barometer is also fitted with a floating gauge to improve its accuracy. It comprises an ivory cylinder cut open at the front and the centre marked with a line; an ivory stem is passed through the cylinder with a float at the bottom end and this rests on the mercury. The float is held in place by a housing that is fixed to the top of the cistern by an ivory screw. The ivory stem is also marked with a ring and the mercury in the cistern is raised by the adjustable screw until both lines coincide. This is known as the neutral point and from which all readings should be taken.

Jesse Ramsden is generally credited with the invention of the floating gauge around 1770, but this is disputed by George Adams in 'A Short Dissertation on the Barometer, Thermometer and other Meteorological Instruments' published in 1790. He writes:

. . . This is effected by means of a floating gauge, which was first applied to the barometer by my Father [George Adams], though others have, since his time, assumed the merit to themselves. By means of the floating gauge the same screw that renders the barometer portable, regulates the surface of the mercury in the cistern, so that it is always at the place from whence the divisions on the scale commence.

The barometer in *Fig.* 71 was made by John Dollond or his son Peter (1730–1820). John was born in 1706 and was first a silk weaver, but he became interested in scientific instruments and opened a workshop for optical instruments with Peter in 1752 in the Strand. They were both well known for making instruments of high quality and it was said that Peter Dollond went down to the glasshouse and picked out all the flawless pieces of flint glass for his workshop.

When the inquisitive French mathematician, Jean Bernoulli, went round the Dollond workshop in 1768, he was shocked to find that instruments stamped with the name Dollond had not actually been made by them, as purchasers imagined. They employed a large number of craftsmen who worked under their direction and supervision, carrying out their original designs. The demand for their instruments was very wide and included observatories in Cassel, Göttingen, Mannheim, Vienna, Stockholm and Geneva.

The trade card of Henry Pyefinch, which he used around 1770, is illustrated in *Fig.* 73. It gives the sale prices of all his instruments and suggests that his barometer shown in *Fig.* 74 would have sold for £3 3s. It has a veneered mahogany case with a triangular or unbroken pediment, obviously copied from the pediments surmounting the cornices of bookcases, cupboards and cabinets which were popular between 1675 and 1760. The reeding of the lower half of the cistern cover is also typical of the same period.

The Fahrenheit mercury thermometer is unusual in that the scale extends from $-30°$ to $212°$ and there are an unusual number of temperature indications engraved on the scale: $32°$ – Freezing; $55°$ – Temperate; $76°$ – Summer Heat; $98°$ – Blood Heat; $112°$ – Fever Heat; $144°$ – Melt Wax;

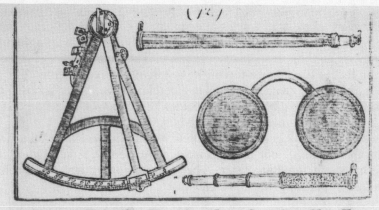

(72)

A C A T A L O G U E

O F

Optical, Philosophical, and Mathematical Instruments,

MADE AND SOLD BY

H E N R Y   P Y E F I N C H,

At the Golden Quadrant, Sun, and Spectacles, No. 67, between *Bishopsgate-Street*,
and the *Royal-Exchange*, in *Cornhill*, L O N D O N.

	l. s. d.
A PAIR best silver spectacles for the temples	0 15 0
Best ditto, with double joints	1 4 0
Brazil pebbles, in silver frame	1 11 6
Ditto, in a double joint frame	1 18 0
Pebbles in best steel frame	1 1 0
Ditto in a double jointed frame	1 4 0
Best steel spectacles for the temples	0 6 6
Ditto	0 5 0
Ditto	0 2 6
Double jointed best steel	0 9 0
Best silver spectacles for nose	0 7 0
Tortoiseshell and silver	0 3 6
Spectacles for the nose	0 1 0
Spectacle cases from 1s. to	1 4 0
Concave glass for short-sighted persons, in horn	0 1 6
Same in tortoiseshell	0 3 0
In tortoiseshell and silver	0 5 6
Ditto	0 10 6
In Pearl and silver	0 12 0
Reading glasses mounted in horn, tortoiseshell, tortoiseshell and silver, &c. from 2s. 6d to	1 11 6
Opera glasses, from 6s. 10	1 1 0
Ditto, nourse skin and silver	1 11 6
Larger 2l. 2s. and	2 12 6
Refracting telescopes for sea and land, with a-chromatic moving object glasses, 20 inches	1 11 6
Two feet	2 2 0
Three feet	3 3 0
and so in proportion to any length	
Refracting telescopes, with fix glasses, two feet long	0 18 0
Three feet, ditto	1 4 0
Four feet, ditto	1 11 6
Refracting telescopes, with 4 glasses, 3 feet painted tube	0 5 0
Three feet in mahogany	0 7 6
Ditto	0 10 6
Refracting telescopes for pocket, of all sorts and sizes, from 5s. to	1 11 6
Reflecting telescopes, for the pocket	2 12 6
Fourteen inches long	5 5 0
Eighteen inches	7 7 0

	l. s. d.
Two feet long	10 10 0
Ditto, with rack work, finder, &c.	16 16 0
Best compound microscope	6 6 0
Ditto, with joint	7 7 0
Ditto, with three pillars	4 4 0
Small sort, ditto	2 12 6
Wilson's microscope	2 2 0
The same adapted for opake objects	2 10 0
Solar microscope compleat	5 5 0
Ditto with magnifiscope	8 8 0
Opake microscope	2 2 0
Prisms, 8s. to	0 18 0
Magic lanthern	1 1 0
Painted figures for ditto	0 5 0
Others from 7s. 6d. to	0 10 6
Concave and convex mirrors of all dimensions from 9s. to	31 10 0
Cylindrical concave	1 1 0
Ditto, larger	1 11 6
Cylindrical convex, and its six pictures	2 12 0
A pocket camera	0 10 0
Ditto, larger	0 15 0
Camera obscura, in form of a book, the best	4 4 0
The same adapted to view prints	5 5 0
Diagonal mirror, or optic machine	0 15 0
Ditto, for two people	1 11 6
Ditto, in form of book,	1 15 0
The best coloured views pasted, at per dozen	0 18 0

Mathematical Instruments.

	l. s. d.
Hadley's octant	1 10 0
Ditto, ivory Ar. and Nonius	2 2 0
Ditto, brass index	2 12 6
Ditto in ebony	3 3 0
Small brass octant	2 12 0
Twelve inch ditto	5 5 0
Eighteen inch ditto edge bars	10 10 0
Davis's and all other quadrants, from 5s. to	0 12 0
Theodolites, from 5l. 5s. to	25 0 0
Circumferenter	2 10 0
Plane table, ball, socket, and staff	3 10 0
Gunter's chains and measuring tapes, of all prices	
Cases with drawing Instruments, from 7s. 6d. to	9 9 0

	l. s. d
Protractors from 1s. 6d. to	4 4 0
Proportional compasses	1 5 0
Ditto larger	1 10 0
Pantographer in ebony	2 12 6
Pantographer, all brass	4 14 6
Gunner's callipers	1 11 6
Parallel rules, from 3s. 6d. to	2 12 6
Horizontal sun dials, 6s. to	10 10 0
Ring dial universal	0 12 0
Ditto, fix inches diameter	0 18 0
Nine inches, best	5 5 0
Ditto on pedestal, very curious	20 0 0
Azimuth compasses	5 5 0
and all other sorts and inferior prices	
Artificial magnets, to lift any weight not exceeding three hundred	1 1 0 / 2 2 0 / 3 3 0
Perambulator, or measuring wheel	6 6 0
Astronomical quadrants, from 15l. 15s. to	150 0 0
Globes 17 inches, the pair	6 6 0
Twelve inches	3 3 0
Nine inches	2 2 0
Six inches	1 11 6
Three inches, for pockets	0 9 0

Philosophical Instruments.

	l. s. d
Best barometer	1 11 6
Ditto	2 2 0
Barometer with thermometer	2 12 6
The same with thermometer and hygrometer	3 3 0
Best sort	4 4 0
Fahrenheit's best thermometer	1 11 6
Ditto	1 1 0
Botanic thermometer	1 1 0
Ditto for	0 16 0
Best hydrometer, with all its weights	1 1 0
Hydrostatic balance	1 16 0
An electrical machine	3 13 6
Ditto, large	5 5 0
Electrometers for ditto	0 10 6
Air pump all brass double barrel	3 13 0
Ditto	5 5 0
Ditto, mahogany and brass, large	7 7 0
Ditto, the most compleat	9 9 0
Apparatus for ditto, from 1l. 11s. 6d to	9 9 0
A pirometer to try the expansion of metals	2 12 6

Fig. 73 Trade card of Henry Pyefinch, c. 1770 (*Science Museum, London*).

68

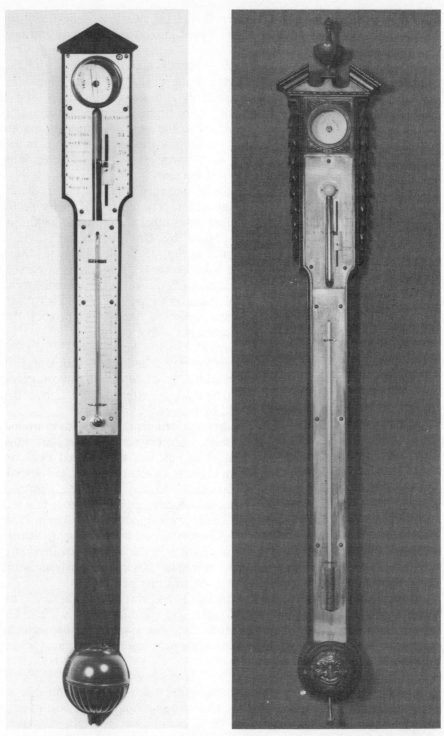

Fig. 74 Mahogany cistern barometer by Pyefinch, London, c. 1770. *Fig.* 75 Mahogany cistern barometer by H. Pyefinch, London, c. 1770 (Crown Copyright, *Victoria and Albert Museum, London*).

176° − Spirits Boil; 212° − Water Boils. The weather indications are standard except that 'Inclined to Fair' is used instead of 'Fair' and 'Inclined to Rain' is substituted for 'Rain'.

Like most other barometer-makers, Pyefinch used an oat beard for his hygrometer. The case is 3 inches wide and the words 'Dry' and 'Moist' are engraved to the left and right, respectively, of the centre. Each side is calibrated from 0 to 30 to show the degree of dryness or moisture above or below the norm. The oat beard is fixed to the centre of the dial and an indicating length of straw is glued to the top of the beard, which is in the shape of a coil. The end attached to the straw will unwind when it is moistened and so rotate the straw round the dial.

The beard has only a limited effective life and very few hygrometers of this type will be found to be in working order. The design of this type of hygrometer hardly varied for a hundred years other than, around 1800, the replacement of the words 'Dry' and 'Moist' by 'Dry' and 'Damp'.

Another Pyefinch barometer is shown in *Fig. 75*. It is probably his 'Best sort' which the trade card shows he sold for £4 4s. The case is of carved mahogany with a broken pediment and the cistern cover is carved in the form of a mask. As in the previous example a bayonet-type tube is used which, in this case, is retained by an ivory cap. A pierced brass cover protects the thermometer, whilst a glazed bezel protects the hygrometer.

Henry Pyefinch traded from 67 Cornhill, London, between 1739 and 1790 and was well known as an optical, philosophical and mathematical instrument-maker. In 1765, in conjunction with J. H. de Magellan, a Portuguese scientist, he patented an instrument to measure the effect of the weight of the atmosphere and the variations caused by heat and cold.

The Troughton family were important instrument-makers from around 1750, and through various partnerships, mergers and takeovers are now known as Vickers Instruments Ltd. The business was started by John Troughton (1716–88) who came from Corney, Cumberland; in 1757 he took a nephew, John Troughton, as an apprentice and they subsequently formed a partnership J. & J. Troughton. John, the nephew, took his brother Edward (1753–1835) as an apprentice in 1773 and they formed a partnership in 1788 under the name J. & E. Troughton. The businesses were in Surrey Street, Strand until 1782 when the Troughtons took over the business of Benjamin Cole at 136 Fleet Street, London. John retired in 1804 and Edward continued alone until 1826 when he took William Simms into partnership.

Edward was the most famous of the family and was quite a character; he never married, was a man of frugal habits and spent most of his life in his back parlour wearing snuff-stained clothes and a wig, with an ear trumpet in his hand. In 1821 a Colonel Hodgson, Surveyor-General in Calcutta, wrote of him:

The instruments made by Mr. Troughton are much more valuable than those made by any other maker in Europe, and though their cost may sometimes be rather more than those of inferior artists, it is well compensated by their exactness and strength, and the peculiar fitness to the purpose for which they are intended.

70

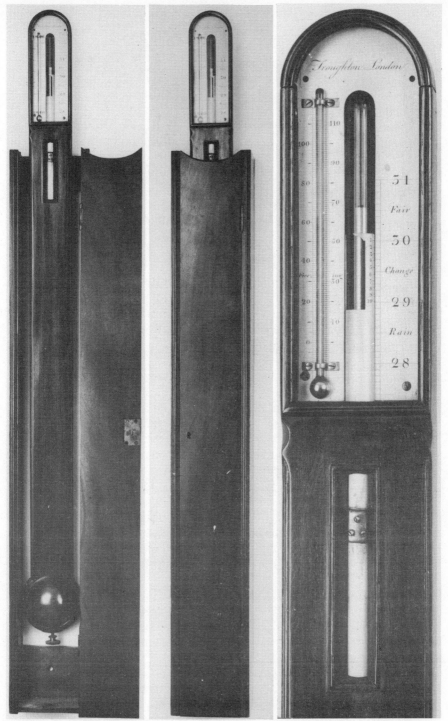

Fig. 76 Mahogany cistern barometer in open case by Troughton, London, c. 1770. *Fig.* 77
Mahogany cistern barometer in closed case by Troughton, London, c. 1770. *Fig.* 78 Detail of *Fig.*
76.

71

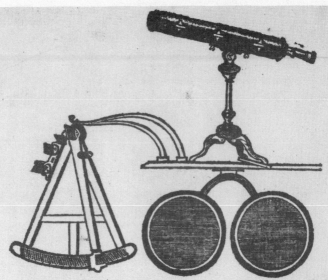

E D W A R D   N A I R N E,

Optical, Philofophical, *and* Mathematical Inftrument-Maker,

At the GOLDEN SPECTACLES, REFLECTING TELESCOPE *and* HADLEY'S QUADRANT, *in* Cornhill, *oppofite the* Royal Exchange, LONDON ;

MAKES and Sells Spe&acles, either of GLASS or BRAZIL PEBBLE, fet in neat and commo-dious Frames, fome of which neither prefs the Nofe nor Temples. CONCAVES for Short-Sighted Perfons; READING, BURNING and MAGNIFYING-GLASSES.

Newtonian and *Gregorian* REFLECTING TELESCOPES ; alfo EQUATORIAL TELESCOPES, or PORTABLE OBSERVATORIES.

REFRACTING TELESCOPES of all Sorts ; particularly one of a new CONSTRUCTION (which may be ufed either at Land or Sea) that will ftand all Kinds of Weather without warping, and is allowed by thofe efteemed the beft JUDGES, who have made feveral late Trials of them at Sea, to exceed all others yet made in *England* ; alfo a peculiar Sort to be ufed at Sea in the Night.

MICROSCOPES, either DOUBLE, SINGLE, AQUATICK, SOLAR, or OPAKE ; likewife a new-invented POCKET MICROSCOPE, that may be ufed with the SOLAR, and anfwers the Purpofes of all the other Sorts.

CAMERA OBSCURAS for delineating Landfkips and Profpe&s (and which ferve to view Perfpe&ive Prints) made with truly Parallel Planes ; SKY-OPTIC BALLS ; PRISMS for demonftrating the Theory of Light and Colours ; CONCAVE, CONVEX, and CYLINDRICAL SPECULUMS ; MAGICK LAN-TERNS ; OPERA GLASSES ; OPTICAL MACHINES for Perfpe&ive Prints ; CYLINDERS and CYLINDRICAL PICTURES.

AIR PUMPS, particularly a fmall Sort that ferves for Condenfing ; AIR FOUNTAINS of various Kinds ; GLASS PUMPS ; WIND GUNS ; PAPIN's DIGESTORS ; alfo a PORTABLE APPARATUS for ELECTRICAL EXPERIMENTS, which is allowed by the CURIOUS to exceed any of the Kind.

BAROMETERS, DIAGONAL, STANDARD, or PORTABLE.

THERMOMETERS, whofe Scales are adjufted to the Bores of their refpe&ive Tubes ; HYGROME-TERS ; HYDROSTATICAL BALANCES, and HYDROMETERS.

HADLEY's QUADRANTS, after the moft exa& Method, with Glaffes, whofe Planes are truly pa-rellel ; DAVIS's QUADRANTS ; GLOBES of all Sizes ; AZIMUTH and other Sea Compaffes ; LOAD-STONES ; NOCTURNALS ; SUN-DIALS of all Sorts ; Cafes of DRAWING INSTRUMENTS ; SCALES ; PARALLEL RULERS ; PROPORTIONAL COMPASSES and DRAWING PENS.

THEODOLITES, SEMICIRCLES, CIRCUMFERENTERS, PLAIN TABLES, DRAWING BOARDS, MEASURING WHEELS, SPIRIT LEVELS, RULES, PENCILS, and all other Sorts of OPTICAL, PHILOSOPHICAL, and MATHEMATICAL INSTRUMENTS, of the neweft and moft approved Inven-tions, are made and fold by the abovefaid *E D W A R D   N A I R N E.*

Fig. 79 Trade card of Edward Nairne, c. 1760 (*Science Museum, London*).

A reviewer of his work writing in the *Philosophical Magazine* stated:

Mr. Troughton stands quite unrivalled in the construction of original astronomical instruments . . . he does and always will hold that rank among makers as Sir Isaac Newton does among philosophers.

An example of a Troughton, London mahogany cistern barometer complete with a protective case is shown in *Figs.* 76–78. The detail shows the delicately moulded frame and the ebony and boxwood stringing round the silvered brass register plates. The engraving is very fine and the vernier is formed at the top of a silvered brass tube, surrounding the barometer tube, which can be raised and lowered by the projection screwed to the brass tube below the register plates. The Troughtons appear to have been content to sign the majority of their instruments 'Troughton, London' so it is difficult to say with any certainty who actually made a particular barometer.

By the third quarter of the eighteenth century the scroll or swan-necked pediment was used from time to time on the cornices of barometers. An example is shown in *Fig.* 71 used by Dollond; it was copied from the pediments that surmounted the cornices of bureau-bookcases and china cabinets of the Chippendale, Hepplewhite and Sheraton periods. The circular section at the top of the scroll or swan neck is sometimes decorated with carved ivory rosettes.

Barometers with rounded tops also began to be made around 1770, being taken from the round-top bookcases and china cabinets which were in vogue during the Sheraton period. This simple form of top persisted, in one form or another, right up until the end of the nineteenth century.

Edward Nairne (1726–1806) favoured the round top and his trade card is illustrated in *Fig.* 79. It shows that he made barometers, diagonal, standard or portable, but it is known that he also made marine barometers as he was responsible for improvements to the tube in 1773 which restricted oscillations in the mercury whilst at sea.

A round-top barometer by Nairne is shown in *Fig.* 80. The mahogany case has brass inlay for decoration and the squared cistern cover is held in position by two screws in the back of the pine frame. The boxwood cistern has no portable screw attachment which suggests that this is one of Nairne's standard barometers.

Fig. 81 illustrates a Nairne portable barometer made around 1770. It has a bayonet-type tube to allow a full-length Fahrenheit mercury thermometer to be mounted on the case. To protect the thermometer bulb there is a brass cover, pierced with diagonal slots to allow the air to flow round the bulb. The hemispherical cistern cover is typical of the ones used until the end of the century.

Edward Nairne was apprenticed to Matthew Loft in 1741 and was elected a Fellow of the Royal Society in 1776. He published various booklets on his navigational, astronomical and pneumatic instruments and in 1772 invented an 'electrical machine' with a horizontal glass cylinder which proved very popular. In 1760 he took Thomas Blunt as an apprentice and made him a

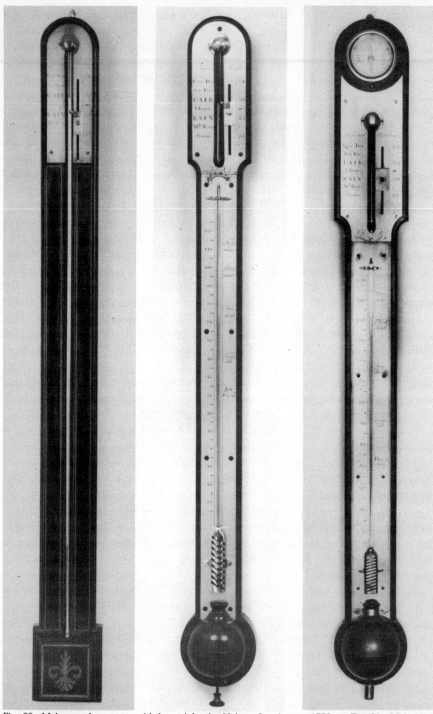

Fig. 80 Mahogany barometer with brass inlay by Nairne, London, c. 1770.   *Fig.* 81 Mahogany cistern barometer by Nairne, London, c. 1770 (*Patric Capon, London*).   *Fig.* 82 Mahogany cistern barometer with hygrometer by Nairne & Blunt, London, c. 1780 (*Antony Preston Antiques Ltd, Stow-on-the-Wold*).

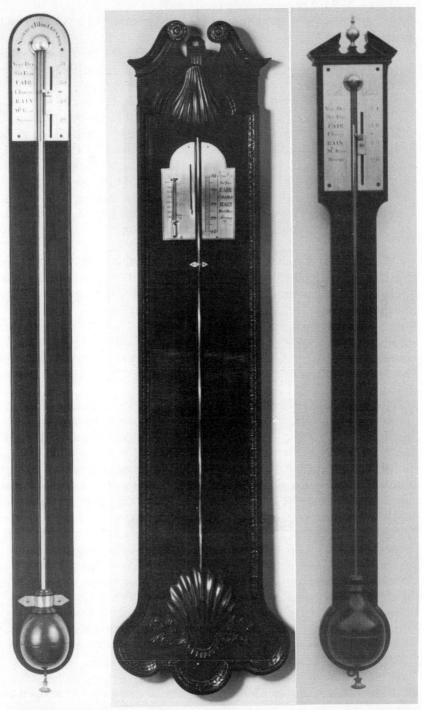

Fig. 83 Mahogany cistern barometer by Nairne & Blunt, London, c. 1790.   *Fig.* 84 Mahogany bulb cistern barometer with decoration in the form of carved scallop shells, rosettes and gadrooning. Unsigned, c. 1775 (*Mallett & Son (Antiques) Ltd, London*).   *Fig.* 85 Mahogany cistern barometer by Dollond, London, c. 1780.

partner in 1774. The partnership lasted until the death of Nairne in 1806, but it appears that whilst in partnership both Nairne and Blunt continued their own individual businesses using their sole names.

A barometer by Nairne & Blunt is illustrated in *Fig.* 82. It is very similar to the Nairne instrument just discussed except that it is fitted with an adjustable oat-beard hygrometer. The adjustment is made by a key through the aperture below the hygrometer bezel.

Fig. 85 shows a typical example of the type of common cistern portable barometer on sale in 1780. The plain mahogany veneered case, hemispherical cistern cover, unadorned register plates and vernier are all representative of this period. The unusual spherical-shaped finial is often seen on barometers by Dollond. Under the silvered brass register plates there is still a piece of paper with the scale divisions and weather indications carefully marked. This was, no doubt, prepared by Dollond and passed to the engravers who inscribed the plates. Peter Dollond was the maker around 1780.

A very similar barometer is illustrated in *Fig.* 86, the only difference being that it has a Fahrenheit thermometer on the register plates, and the maker's name 'G. Adams, Fleet Street, London' is engraved in a cartouche above the tube cap. This is George Adams junior.

Another important group of instrument-makers active from the middle of the eighteenth century was the Watkins family. The business was started by Francis Watkins in Charing Cross in 1747 and today, by subsequent amalgamations and takeovers, forms part of the GEC–Elliott Automation Group.

The mahogany barometer shown in *Fig.* 88 was made around 1780 by Francis Watkins. The case has moulded edges and is decorated with ebony and boxwood stringing. There is an adjustable hygrometer above the silvered brass register plates with the surrounds adorned with boxwood.

Another mahogany cistern barometer by Watkins is illustrated in *Figs.* 89 and 90. It is very like the previous instrument except that it has a perpetual almanac in place of the hygrometer. The days of the month are fixed, but the days of the week can be adjusted up or down by a rack-and-pinion mechanism so that, at the beginning of each month, the days of the week can be set against the appropriate days of the month. A similar mechanism is used to allow each month to appear in turn with the days in that particular month. Watkins was best known for a type of angle barometer which included a 'Perpetual Regulation of Time'; these are discussed in chapter 7.

Instrument-making in Scotland did not make much headway until early in the eighteenth century, so it is not surprising that only a few Scottish barometer-makers are recorded. One notable Scottish maker was William Robb who is recorded as being a long-case clockmaker in Montrose in 1776 and appears to have been active until 1816. He is best known for his double-angle barometers, one of which is illustrated in chapter 7, but an open cistern type made by him is shown in *Fig.* 91. The case is veneered with mahogany with a hemispherical cistern cover in two sections so that the top half can be removed. The top of the tube is held in position by a scroll decoration whilst

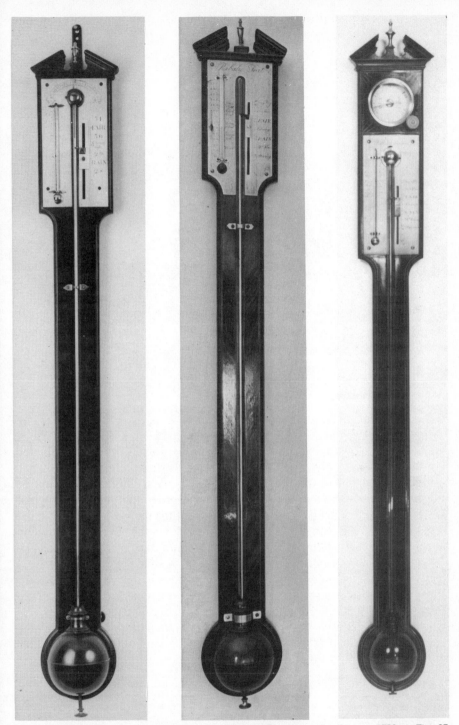

Fig. 86 Mahogany cistern barometer by G. Adams, Fleet Street, London, c. 1780. *Fig.* 87 Mahogany cistern barometer with herring-bone veneer by Rabalio, c. 1780 (*H. W. Keil Ltd, Broadway*). *Fig.* 88 Mahogany cistern barometer with hygrometer by Watkins, London, c. 1780 (*Phillips, London*).

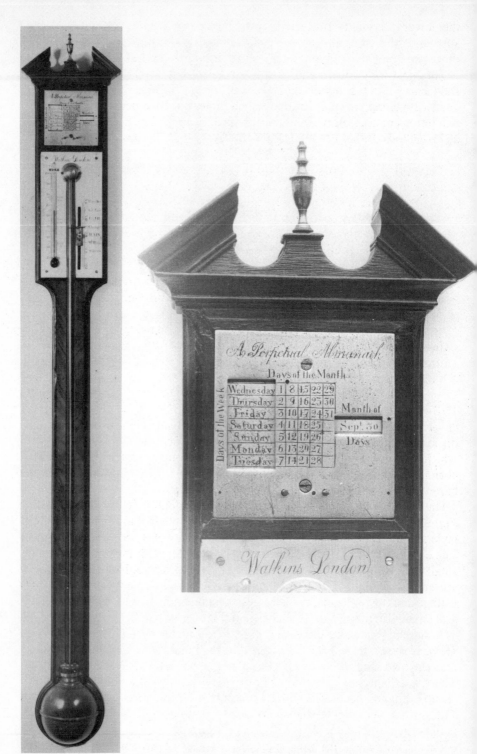

Fig. 89 Mahogany cistern barometer with a perpetual almanac by Watkins, London, c. 1780. *Fig.* 90
Detail of *Fig.* 89.

the lower section is protected by a mahogany sheath. A moulded rim surrounds the case and the register plates, and the pediment is similar to those seen on English barometers some fifty years earlier.

The most well-known and prolific maker of barometers in Scotland was Balthazar Knie. It is believed that he was born in Germany and spent several years travelling around Europe as an itinerant barometer-maker giving exhibitions of glassblowing. It appears that he arrived in Edinburgh in 1776 as his advertisement in the *Caledonian Mercury* on 13 April 1776 reads:

Balthazar Knie, Artist, hereby informs the curious that he is now in Edinburgh, at his lodgings, 2nd door above Mr. Scyth, upholsterer, facing Niddry's Wynd, where he makes Barometers and Thermometers, of any invention that can be thought of; and in particular makes a short diagonal Barometer, quicker and more visible than any upright one. He will give his work out upon trial and is assured, from the success he has already had, of giving satisfaction. He makes four minute and three minute Glasses (the proper time for boiling an egg); also; half minute and quarter minute Glasses, all in one piece, proper for shipmasters.

N.B. He blows and spins glass before company on the table, and forms many curiosities too tedious to mention. If any of the curious have in mind to see him at work, they are heartily welcome, from six to eight in the evening. His stay in this city will be short.

Knie's stay in Edinburgh, however, was far from short; he remained there, at various addresses, until he died in 1817. He intended to retire in 1814 and dispose of his stock by way of a lottery; he valued the stock at £309 14s, which comprised some 70 instruments, but the lottery appears to have been abandoned through lack of support as he was still making and repairing barometers and thermometers in 1815.

One of his bulb cistern barometers made around 1790 is illustrated in *Fig. 92.* The case is veneered with mahogany in the herring-bone or feather style and the edges are decorated with ebony and boxwood zebra stringing. The oval cistern cover was favoured by several Scottish makers, as was the small flat entablature above the domed silvered brass register plates. These are engraved 'Knie Edin.' in a narrow cartouche decorated with trailing leafage and flower heads, the latter also ornament the two lower screws. The scale extends from 27 to 31 inches and the overall height is 39 inches.

A similar, but more elaborate, cistern barometer by Knie, made around 1800, is shown in *Fig. 93.* The case differs in that it has a chamfered rather than an oval cistern cover and the plates are protected by a glazed door. There is a Fahrenheit thermometer on the silvered scale which is engraved 'Knie Edin' and decorated with an urn of flowers and three compass motifs. The vernier has a sickle-shaped pointer. A double-angle barometer by Knie is illustrated in chapter 7.

Barometer cases with bow fronts and urn-shaped cistern covers became a popular feature during the third quarter of the eighteenth century and an

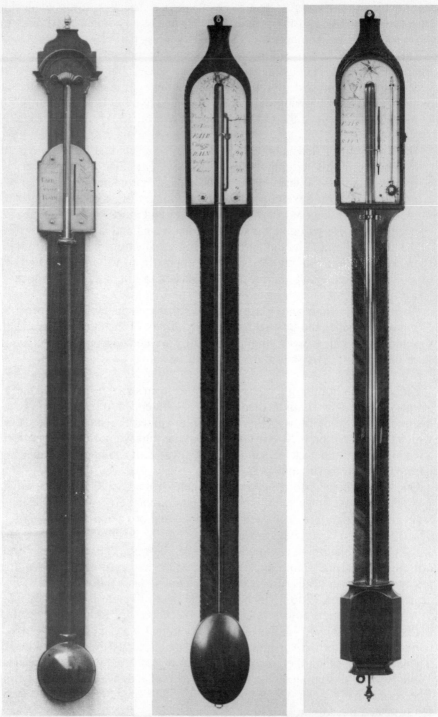

Fig. 91 Mahogany open cistern barometer by William Robb, c. 1780 (*Peter D. Bosson, Wilmslow*).
Fig. 92 Mahogany bulb cistern barometer by Knie, Edinburgh, c. 1790. *Fig.* 93 Mahogany portable cistern barometer by Knie, Edinburgh, c. 1800 (*Sotheby's, London*).

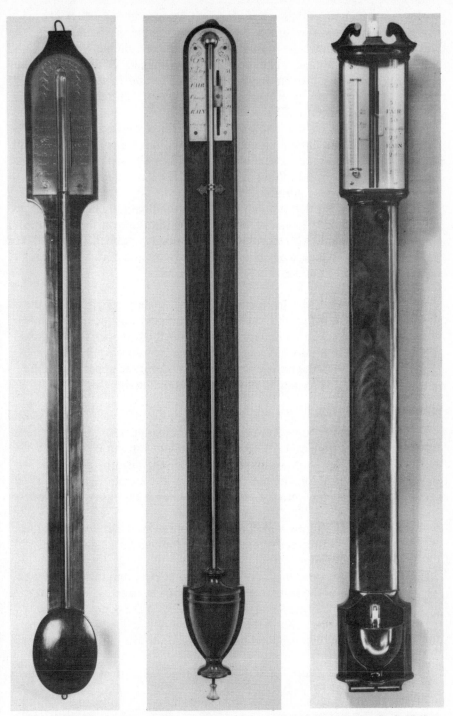

Fig. 94 Mahogany bulb cistern barometer with summer and winter weather indications by C. Moliner, fl. 1784–1801 (*Lalonde Bros & Parham, Bristol*). *Fig.* 95 Mahogany cistern barometer with round top and urn-shaped cistern cover by Smith, Bath, c. 1790. *Fig.* 96 Mahogany cistern barometer with bow front and ivory float by Troughton, London, c. 1780 (*Hotspur Ltd, London*).

instrument with both of these characters is illustrated in *Fig*. 96. It was made by J. & E. Troughton in Surrey Street, Strand, London around 1780. The bow-fronted case allows the maker to emphasise the light and highly grained mahogany to advantage. The ebonised urn-shaped cistern cover was probably copied from the urn shapes on the door furniture, wall hangings and mantelpieces designed by Robert Adam, following his return to England from Italy and France in 1758.

Bowed glass protects the silvered brass register plates and this can only be removed by lifting off the moulded cornice and scroll pediment which is a separate unit. This makes it necessary to fit a key below the hood to adjust the vernier by a rack-and-pinion mechanism. The key is detachable and also used to turn the cistern portable screw.

This barometer is fitted with an ivory float or floating gauge of the type described by George Adams in 'A Short Dissertation on the Barometer, Thermometer and other Meteorological Instruments' published in 1790. He points out that this gauge is never applied to the common portable barometer, but only to those of the best kind, and continues:

The gauge consists of a small stem of ivory, arising from a float of the same substance; a circular division is cut round this stem; the stem passes through a short cylinder of ivory, which is cut open in front; on this front two small divisions are cut; at the bottom of this cylinder is a male screw, to fit the female screw of the cistern; the upper part of the gauge is protected by a tube of glass perforated at the top.

To Use the Barometer.
1. The barometer being fixed in a perpendicular position, unscrew the screw at bottom as far as it will go without forcing it.
2. Take out the ivory screw at the top of the cistern, and place it between the scrolls on the upper part of the frame.
3. Screw the gauge into the place from whence the ivory screw was taken.
4. Screw up the screw which is at the bottom of the frame, until the line on the float exactly coincides with the two lines on the front of the ivory cylinder.
5. Strike the barometer gently with the knuckles, and then so set the lower edge of the front index to the convex surface of the mercury, that it may be at the same time in a line with the edge of the index behind the tube; and the nonius [vernier] will then give the true height of the mercurial column, from the surface of the mercury in the cistern.
6. The preceding rule for setting the gauge must be complied with, previous to every observation.

It is difficult to see the glass tube protecting the gauge in the illustration, or the ivory screw between the scrolls of the pediment.

Fig. 97 shows a similar barometer by Jesse Ramsden, but not the 'best

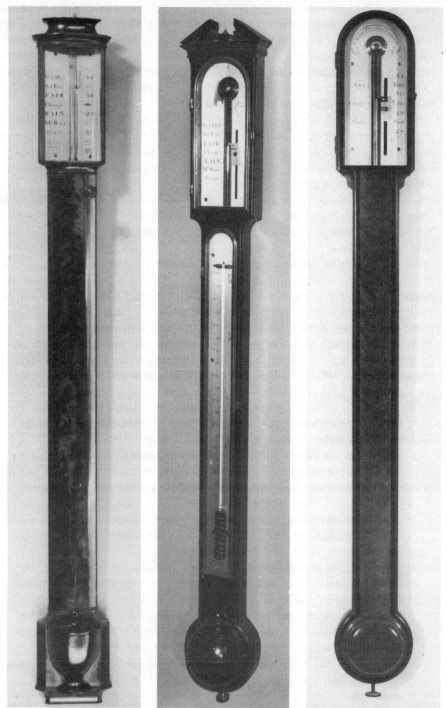

Fig. 97   Mahogany bow-fronted cistern barometer with squared and moulded top by Ramsden, London, c. 1785 (*Hotspur Ltd, London*).   *Fig.* 98   Mahogany cistern barometer and thermometer by Dollond, London, c. 1790 (*Peter Hunwick, Hungerford*).   *Fig.* 99   Mahogany cistern barometer by G. Adams, Fleet Street, London, c. 1790 (*M. W. Cox, Bristol*).

83

sort' as it has no thermometer or ivory float. However, the grain of the mahogany on the bow-fronted case makes it a very attractive piece of furniture. The squared and moulded cornice became popular around 1780 and was used by various makers for fifty years. The cistern cover is square with bevelled edges, which are fluted, with an urn in relief to give depth to the cistern area. The tube is hidden within the panelled case and is not fixed to the centre of the boxwood cistern.

Towards the end of the eighteenth century it became common practice to protect the register plates with glass; this usually took the form of a hinged glazed door which could be opened by a brass knob, so that the vernier could be adjusted before taking a reading. The glass also gave protection to the thermometer if it was mounted on the register plates.

Alternatively, the thermometer was fitted to the trunk of the barometer in its own glazed case as shown in *Fig.* 98. Both barometer and thermometer have hinged brass glazed doors, but usually the thermometer case is fixed. It was made by Peter Dollond around 1790.

A change in the shape of the cistern cover also took place in the last decade or so of the eighteenth century. The majority of those made previously were hemispherical but around 1790 the covers became more shallow, as in *Fig.* 99, and were often inlaid with a darker wood or ivory rings. This is a plain portable barometer veneered in mahogany with moulded edges and ebonised stringing. It was made by George Adams junior in Fleet Street, London, about the same time as he published his 'Short Dissertation on the Barometer' in 1790. At the end of the Dissertation he appended a list of meteorological instruments made and sold by him which included:

A Plain portable barometer	£2 2s. 0d.
Ditto with a thermometer	£3 3s. 0d.
A plain barometer, covered frame and glass doors	£2 12s. 6d.
Ditto with a thermometer	£3 13s. 6d.
A barometer with a long cylindrical thermometer	£4 4s. 0d.
A ditto with ditto and De Luc's hygrometer	£7 7s. 0d.
A barometer and thermometer, with a gauge, the indexes moving by rack-work	£5 15s. 0d.
Ditto neater	£6 16s. 6d.
A barometer for measuring the altitude of mountains, etc.	£9 9s. 0d.
Marine barometers	—
Diagonal, wheel, and statical barometers	—

In the Preface he described his Dissertation as a 'Hastily written tract' which 'would be an acceptable present to my customers', but it comprises some sixty pages and gives considerable information on the barometers made in the 1780s. His opening paragraph states:

There is scarce any subject in which mankind feel themselves more interested than the weather, the temperature of the air, and the influences of wind and rain; which is evident, from its constantly

Fig. 100 Oak bulb cistern barometer with paper plates by Manticha, London, c. 1780. *Fig.* 101 Detail of *Fig.* 100.

85

forming a principal topic of conversation. The traveller endeavours to regulate his motions, and the farmer his operations, by the weather: by it, plenty or famine is dispensed, and millions are furnished with the necessaries of life.

He is critical of some makers:

The scale should be of some known measure. It would have been totally unnecessary to have mentioned this condition, had it not been to prevent those, into whose hands this tract may fall, from being imposed upon by vendors of imperfect instruments. Some of these instruments have no determinate scale affixed to them; and those which have a scale, have one that is in general ill graduated and erroneously placed, so that no comparative observations can be made with them; and often, indeed, no observations at all; as from the small bore of the tube, they act as a thermometer, as well as a barometer.

On signs from animals:

Those who pay attention to the animal creation, will find in their habitudes, many prognostics of the changes of the weather. In the nature of their labours, by the uneasiness they testify, by the peculiar tone of their voice, or by the precautions they take to shelter themselves, their feelings are probably more acute, and their senses more awake to the delicate impressions of natural causes, than ours, where the mind by its continual action diminishes the force of all external impressions.

The vast majority of barometers made during the eighteenth and the first half of the nineteenth century had silvered brass register plates, but occasionally the plates were printed on paper which was then varnished. They were sometimes favoured by country makers, but were not used on any particular design until the last quarter of the eighteenth century when paper plates became the rule on barometers of the design shown in *Figs.* 100 and 101.

The case is of panelled oak with side pillars supporting the moulded flat cornice. A bulb cistern is used and access is obtained by unscrewing the base of the cistern cover. The weather indications are a mixture of Gothic, Roman and copperplate writing with decoration of entwined leaves, grapes, flowers and winged cherubs. The plates are protected by glass which is placed in position through a slot in the top of the cornice. A twisted wire pointer is operated manually up and down a brass rod behind the right-hand pillar.

The barometer was made around 1780 by Dominick Manticha of 11 Ely Court, Holborn, London. He was one of the many Italians who migrated from Holland and France around 1770. At that time there were a large number of Italians established in these two countries as glassblowers and instrument-makers, including barometers, having arrived from Italy almost a hundred years earlier. Their arrival in London had a significant influence on the design of the wheel barometer.

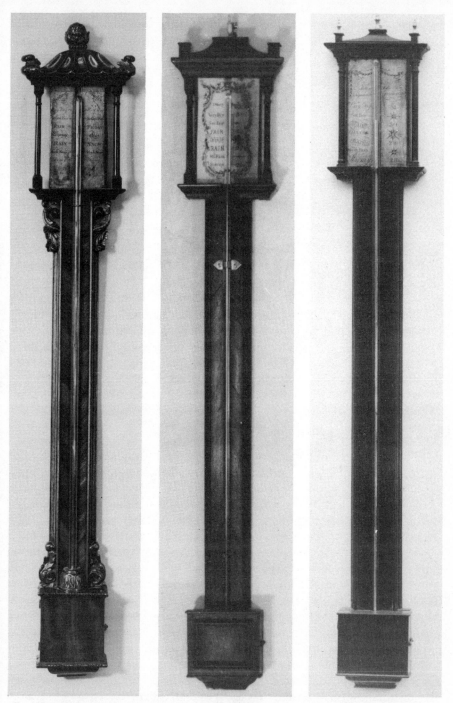

Fig. 102 Mahogany bulb cistern barometer by T. L. Polti, Leeds, c. 1790 (*Mallett & Son (Antiques) Ltd, London*).   *Fig.* 103 Mahogany bulb cistern barometer with paper plates by J. Merry Roncketi, c. 1790 (*H. W. Keil Ltd, Broadway*).   *Fig.* 104 Mahogany bulb cistern barometer with paper plates by Mathew Woller, Edgbaston Street, Birmingham, c. 1800.

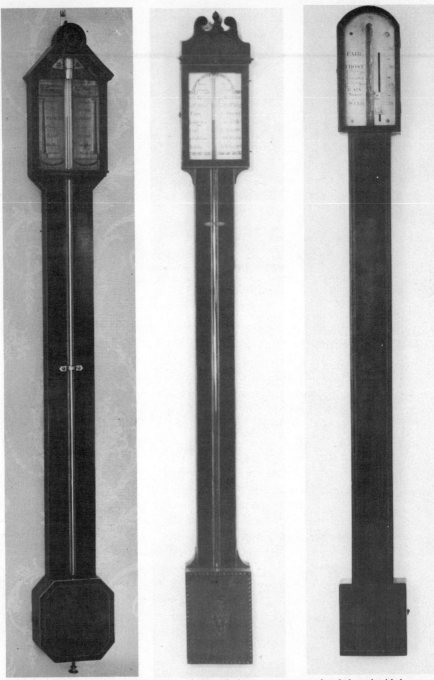

Fig. 105 Mahogany cistern barometer with hinged cistern cover, cross-banded, and with boxwood stringing. Paper plates with summer and winter weather indications. Unsigned, c. 1800 (*H. W. Keil Ltd, Broadway*). *Fig.* 106 Mahogany bulb cistern barometer with boxwood stringing. Rectangular cistern cover is bordered with zebra stringing and inset with a marquetry panel of oak leaves. Paper plates signed 'Made by James Frank', 41 inches high, c. 1800 (*Phillips, London*). *Fig.* 107 Mahogany cistern barometer with round top and squared cistern cover. Tunbridge ware marquetry decoration by A. Bellamy, Wycombe, 1799.

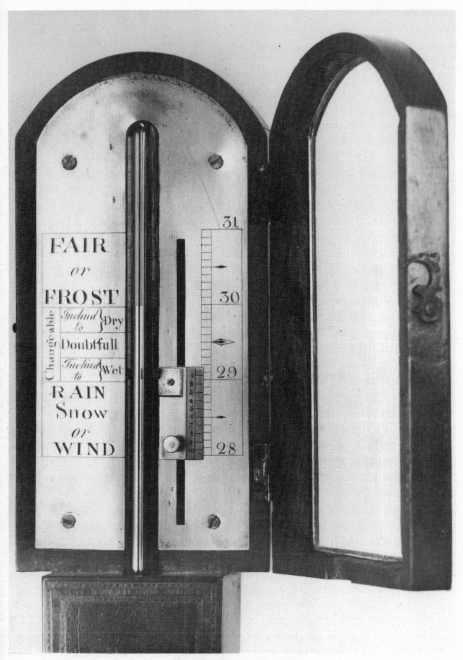

Fig. 108 Detail of *Fig.* 107.

Bulb cistern barometers were far more popular on the Continent than in England and it could well be that the Italians brought this design of barometer with them. *Fig.* 102 illustrates a similar barometer but in a far more elegant mahogany case. The pillared hood is a reminder of earlier clock-case designs whilst the decoration and pagoda-type pediment suggests the Chinese Chippendale influence of 1765–70. The bulb cistern is contained within a shallow hinged box and the tube is held in place by wire threaded through from the back of the case. There are summer and winter weather indications on the paper plates which are signed T. L. Polti, Leeds. Whilst the majority of Italians stayed in London, a few settled in the large provincial towns and cities before the end of the century. This could be the maker who signed his barometers 'Polti from Italy'.

The common type of printed paper plate barometer made around the turn of the century is shown in *Fig.* 103. The moulded case has a feathered mahogany veneer with a pagoda-type pediment over ogee cresting. A moulding decorates the squared box which contains a bulb cistern. The barometer scale is surrounded by a festoon of leaves and flowers and is signed 'J. Merry Roncketi, Fecit'. He was another Italian immigrant who settled in London and was established in Holborn by 1790, making weather-glasses, where he was active for thirty years.

This type of barometer had no pretensions to being an accurate instrument; it had no vernier and many had no pointer or set hand. It was accepted that the bulb cistern tube was not as accurate as the portable cistern tube, because there was no way of maintaining the level of the mercury in the bulb cistern. However, they were cheap, attractive and popular to the extent that several English makers copied them.

An example is given in *Fig.* 104, made by Mathew Woller who was a clock and barometer-maker at 51 Edgbaston Street, Birmingham, and active between 1800 and 1828. The veneered mahogany case has moulded edges and the pagoda pediment has three brass finials. The paper plates have standard weather indications and are decorated with two flying cherubs and trailing garlands of leaves. The plates are protected by glass which is fixed flush against them.

An unusual cistern barometer is illustrated in *Figs.* 107 and 108. The solid mahogany case is veneered with mahogany and decorated with ebony and boxwood stringing round the glazed door. Tunbridge ware marquetry is used round the trunk and cistern cover. The case is open at the back to receive the tube. The silvered brass register plates are particularly interesting as 'Changeable' has been split into 'Inclind to Dry', 'Doubtfull' and 'Inclind to Wet'. Identical words appear on the barometer illustrated in *Fig.* 45 made around 1740 but this instrument appears to have been made in 1799 as this date is written in ink on the back of the case and numbered '2'. The name A. Bellamy, Wycombe, is written above the date and he almost certainly was the maker.

5

Regency and William IV, 1800–37

Up until the nineteenth century, instrument-makers were considered to be an elite society who produced attractive and functional instruments. They were craftsmen in closed societies of Guilds and Companies, living in close communities. This continued to some extent in the nineteenth century, but with the introduction of mass-production techniques the practice of contracting out components, such as thermometers and hygrometers, to specialist makers was widespread. In spite of these changes there were no noticeable improvements in the quality or accuracy of barometers and very little change in the designs. Component parts became more standardised and this led, in some cases, to a deterioration in quality. The scroll, broken and flat moulded pediments continued to be used and the urn-shaped cistern cover was popular during the Regency period.

Fig. 109 illustrates a cistern barometer by Beilby, Bristol, veneered with an attractively grained mahogany on a pinewood case. An ebonised urn-shaped cistern cover is used, and there is a broad band of matching ebonised stringing right round the case; the mouldings on the front of the pediment scrolls are also ebonised. This suggests that the barometer was made shortly after the death of Lord Nelson in 1805, as ebony decoration was often used by cabinet-makers after his death as a mark of respect for him. The urn finial and the rosettes on the scroll pediment are of ivory.

A cistern barometer with a bow-fronted case veneered with mahogany is shown in *Fig.* 110. It also has bowed glass to protect the register plates and a bowed and moulded cornice. The urn-shaped finial seems out of proportion and is probably not original. The barometer was made by Macrae, Royal Exchange, London around 1805.

William Cary (1759–1825), who traded from the Strand in London, made identical barometers. He was an optical and mathematical instrument-maker and supplied monthly meteorological observations to the *Philosophical Magazine*. He was a pupil of Jesse Ramsden and the brother of John Cary the cartographer.

A very similar bow-fronted mahogany barometer is shown in *Fig.* 111, except that it has a moulded and flat cornice. It is signed 'Berge, London late Ramsden'. This was Matthew Berge who took over Jesse Ramsden's business in Piccadilly when he died in 1800. A number of instruments are signed in this way and no doubt Berge was trading on the very high

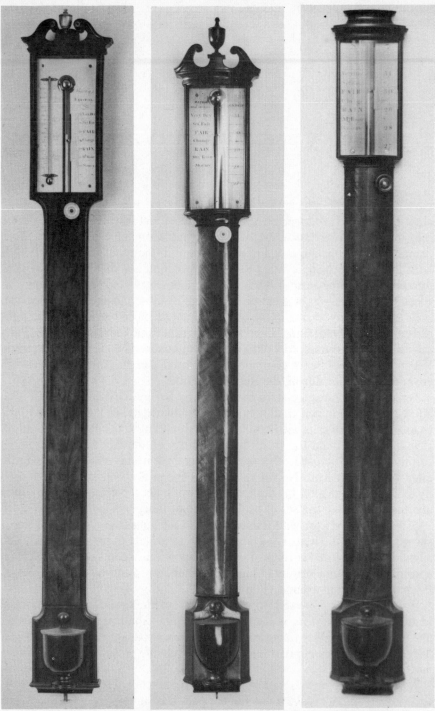

Fig. 109 Mahogany cistern barometer by Beilby, Bristol, c. 1805. *Fig.* 110 Mahogany bow-fronted cistern barometer by Macrae, Royal Exchange, London, c. 1805 (*Peter Heppleston*). *Fig.* 111 Mahogany bow-fronted cistern barometer by Berge, London, late Ramsden, c. 1805 (*Avon Antiques, Bradford-on-Avon*).

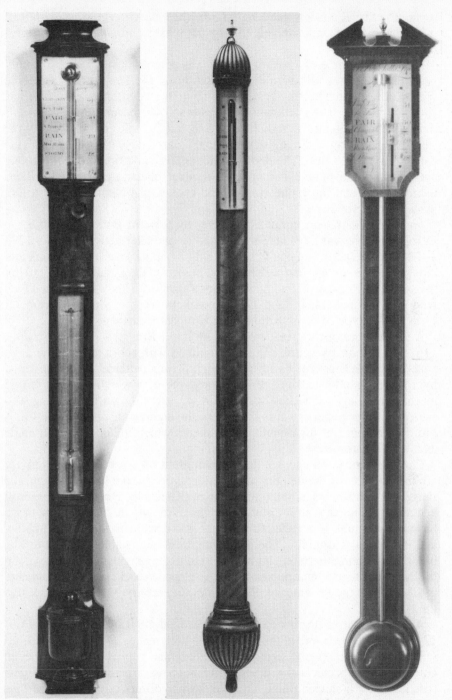

Fig. 112 Mahogany bow-fronted cistern barometer with Fahrenheit thermometer. Silvered register plates and scales by F. Day, 37 Poultry, London, c. 1810.   *Fig.* 113 Mahogany bow-fronted cistern barometer with moulded edges and gadrooned top and base. Silvered register plates, signed A. Adie, Edinburgh, c. 1810 (*Sotheby's, London*).   *Fig.* 114 Mahogany bulb cistern barometer by J. Bapt. Salla, c. 1800.

reputation that Ramsden had built up over the years. Berge was an optical, mathematical and philosophical instrument-maker and was in business for nineteen years.

A typical example of a barometer that was popular during the first twenty years of the nineteenth century is shown in *Fig*. 114. The frame is veneered with mahogany in a herring-bone pattern with moulded edges bordered by a chequered inlay. The shallow turned cistern cover became popular at this time with the bulb cistern tube favoured by Italian makers. A feature of the case is the tapering of the register plates and glazed door to conform with the narrowing of the trunk. The door is also veneered and bordered with ebony and boxwood stringing. The silvered register plates are signed 'J. Bapt. Salla. Fecit', and the broad cornice and broken pediment suggests it was made around 1800.

Fig. 115 illustrates a similar barometer by Edward Butler of Tutbury in Derbyshire. He was a country watch- and clockmaker active between 1795 and 1828. The pine frame is veneered with mahogany across the trunk and moulded edges are applied to the sides. The glazed door is also veneered but the silvered scales have a pointer and not a vernier. This was often the case with country makers; in fact, London makers were producing barometer cases of this type of construction some fifty years earlier.

A much more decorative barometer by Bapt. Roncheti is shown in *Fig*. 116. The mahogany veneered case is outlined with zebra stringing and the panelled trunk is adorned with marquetry flower patterns. The Dry/Moist hygrometer is adjusted by the key below the dial which operates a cog mechanism. Baptis Roncheti was one of the early Italian immigrants who settled in Manchester towards the end of the eighteenth century. He was a prolific producer of high-quality instruments which included wheel, angle and double barometers.

Charles Aiano was another Italian immigrant who settled in Canterbury around the turn of the century and produced decorative barometers with a range of instruments similar to those of Roncheti. He made the scroll pediment mahogany bulb cistern barometer shown in *Fig*. 117. It has a bayonet-type tube in a panelled case decorated with marquetry and ebony and boxwood stringing. The hygrometer is adjustable, and both the barometer and the thermometer have glazed mahogany doors. Aiano's main business was that of an optician but he also made clocks and thermometers at 'The sign of the Providence', Northgate, Canterbury, where he was active until 1840.

A Scottish barometer which was made around 1800 is illustrated in *Figs*. 121 and 122. The frame of the case is pine with mahogany veneer bordered with ebony and boxwood stringing. The base and capital of the Corinthian column which protects the tube are of brass as are the scroll pediment rosettes and urn-shaped finial. The oval-shaped cistern cover was used by a number of Scottish makers. The silvered brass register plates are very similar to the type used by Benjamin Martin in that the barometer, thermometer and hygrometer are each entitled. In this case the hygrometer was an oat beard. The overall height is 43 inches.

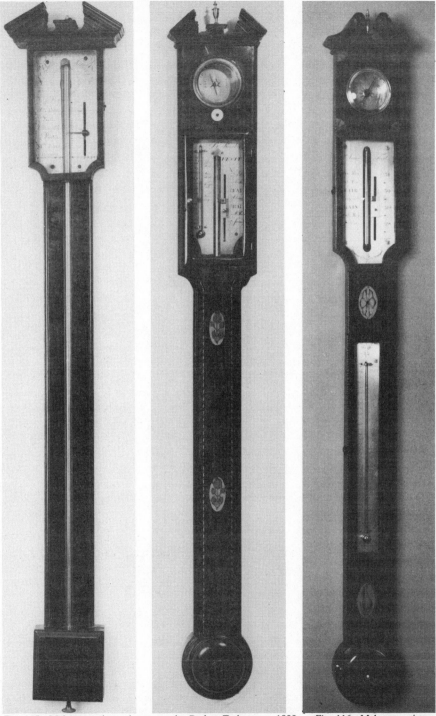

Fig. 115 Mahogany cistern barometer by Butler, Tutbury, c. 1800.   *Fig.* 116 Mahogany cistern barometer by Bapt. Roncheti, c. 1800.   *Fig.* 117   Mahogany bulb cistern barometer by C. Aiano, c. 1800 (*Peter Hunwick, Hungerford*).

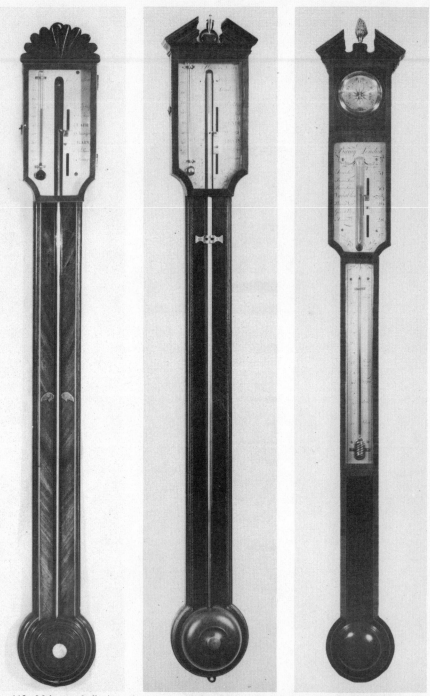

Fig. 118 Mahogany bulb cistern barometer with fan pediment by Joseph Denton, Hull, c. 1805 (*M. W. Cox, Bristol*). *Fig.* 119 Mahogany bulb cistern barometer with herring-bone veneer and chequered inlay by Hardy, 171 Holborn, London, c. 1810. *Fig.* 120 Mahogany bulb cistern barometer with thermometer and adjustable hygrometer all in cross-banded panels. French inscriptions by Barny, London, c. 1810 (*Bonhams, London*).

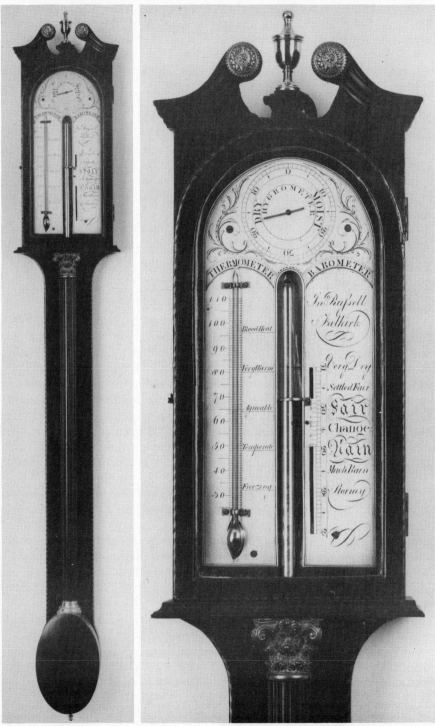

Fig. 121 Mahogany cistern barometer by John Russell, Falkirk, c. 1800. *Fig.* 122 Detail of *Fig.* 121.

97

The maker was John Russell (1745–1817) of Falkirk in Scotland. He was the son of a blacksmith and opened a shop in 1770 where he became renowned for his clocks, watches and musical boxes. It appears that he concentrated on only two types of barometer, the one just described and a distinctive wheel instrument. Russell was appointed watchmaker to the Prince of Wales, later George IV.

An important maker who made barometers until around 1820 was Thomas Blunt, and his trade card is reproduced in *Fig.* 123. He was apprenticed to Edward Nairne in 1760 and became his partner in 1774, trading under the well-known name of Nairne & Blunt. Nairne retired in 1801 but Blunt was joined by his son in the business by 1806. As the trade card shows, Blunt became mathematical instrument-maker to King George III, probably because he designed some of the components of the 'New Barometer' by the Portuguese scientist J. H. de Magellan, used for measuring heights.

A round-top portable cistern barometer by Blunt is illustrated in *Fig.* 124. It is veneered with mahogany in the herring-bone style with an edging of ebonised veneer, probably as a mark of respect on the death of Lord Nelson in 1805. The cistern is protected by an egg-shaped cover which Blunt favoured and used almost exclusively. *Fig.* 125 proves that he used a normal cistern cover occasionally.

The hemispherical cistern cover was used less frequently around 1810, mainly because the bulb cistern tube was becoming more popular and required less cistern depth; this allowed the makers to use a more shallow round turned cover which was easier to produce. There was also a tendency towards standardised designs so that mass-production methods could be employed. The demand for barometers by the general public was still increasing and the leading makers were able to produce them in large numbers at reasonable prices and sell them to retailers; these included opticians and sellers of instruments, looking glasses, furniture and pictures. If the retailer would order a sufficient number at a time then the makers would engrave the name of the retailer on the register plates.

The barometer illustrated in *Fig.* 127 by Jones of Oxford Street, London, around 1810 is representative of the style of the period. The pine case is veneered with mahogany and outlined with ebonised stringing, which extends round the register plate cover and cistern cover. The thermometer case is fixed and the ivory key below the register plates is used to adjust the vernier. A key is necessary as the glass protecting the plates is fixed and can only be removed by detaching the complete cornice section and then sliding the glass upwards.

The decorative trade card of Dudley Adams (c. 1800) is reproduced in *Fig.* 129. It tells us that he made 'all sorts of Optical, Mathematical and Philosophical Instruments, constructed on the best and most approved principles and in the modern manner'. He was 'Globe manufacturer and mathematical instrument maker to His Majesty King of Great Britain, and Optician to His Royal Highness the Prince of Wales'. He describes himself as 'Son of George Adams senior long deceased and brother to the late George Adams at No. 60 Fleet Street, London, where the above business has been carried on for nearly a century'.

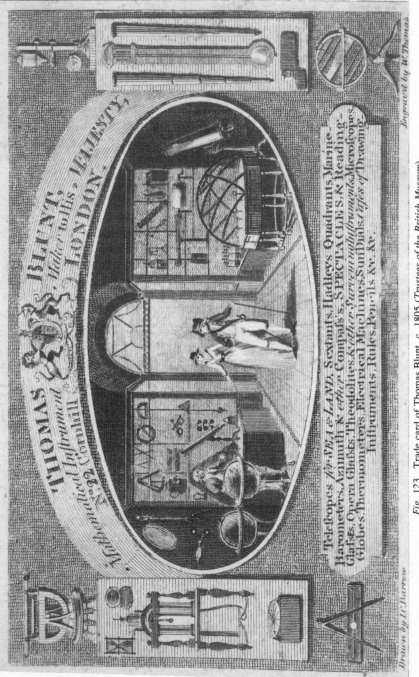

Fig. 123   Trade card of Thomas Blunt, c. 1805 (*Trustees of the British Museum*).

99

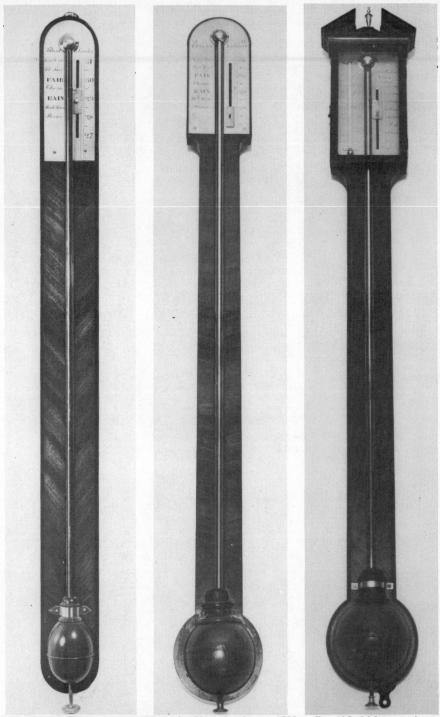

Fig. 124 Mahogany cistern barometer by Blunt, London, c. 1805.   *Fig.* 125 Mahogany cistern barometer by T. Blunt, London, c. 1805 (*Phillips, London*).   *Fig.* 126 Mahogany cistern barometer with herring-bone veneer and moulded edges by John Wisker, York, c. 1805 (*Phillips, London*).

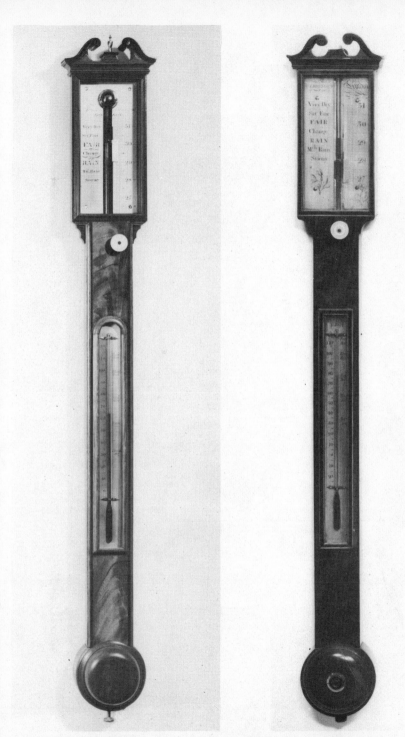

Fig. 127 Mahogany cistern barometer by Jones, 241 Oxford Street, London, c. 1810.   *Fig.* 128
Mahogany bulb cistern barometer with ebony and boxwood stringing. Silvered brass register plates with
flower decoration and shallow turned cistern cover, with ivory rosette. By Berringer, London, c. 1810.

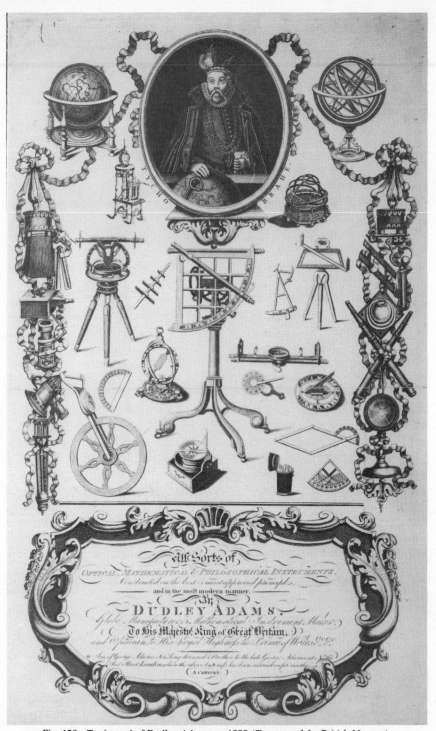

Fig. 129   Trade card of Dudley Adams, c. 1800 (*Trustees of the British Museum*).

Dudley was born in 1762 and apprenticed to his brother in 1777. He was free in 1788 and continued the family business when his brother died in 1795. A son, George Adams, was apprenticed to him in 1811.

An example of his work is shown in *Fig.* 130. It is a portable cistern barometer with the case panelled and veneered with mahogany. The edges of the case are moulded, with a cross-banded border. Both the barometer and thermometer have glazed brass doors and the thermometer bulb is protected by a pierced brass sleeve. The hygrometer has lost its oat beard and straw; note that the scale has the words 'Dry/Damp' engraved on the two 0 to 30 calibrations; these replaced 'Dry/Moist' at the turn of the century.

A barometer of similar outline is shown in *Fig.* 131. The panelled and veneered case is decorated with ebony and boxwood stringing and there is a key to adjust the vernier as the glazed brass surround to the register plates is fixed. An unusual feature is the spirit level set into the cistern cover; these were considered to be an essential refinement to the wheel or banjo barometer from around 1800 but are very rarely seen on cistern barometers. The level is fixed across the centre of an engraved plate protected by a glazed bezel. Its purpose was to ensure that the barometer was hung in an exactly vertical position.

The barometer was made around 1810 by Thomas Rubergall of 27 Coventry Street, London, who was active between 1802 and 1854. He was optician and mathematical instrument-maker to the Duke of Clarence and optician to King George III.

A square hinged box type cistern cover was sometimes used for bulb cistern barometers as an alternative to the shallow round turned cover. *Fig.* 132 illustrates this on a barometer by Tarone, Bristol, made around 1810. The attractively grained mahogany veneer is further adorned by shell and star marquetry and the moulded case is outlined with chequered stringing. A vernier is used with a Fahrenheit thermometer.

Scottish barometer-makers continued to produce barometers in distinctive cases in the nineteenth century, and *Fig.* 137 shows an example of the type of ordinary barometer produced in Scotland during the first quarter of the century.

The mahogany case is veneered with satinwood with moulded and ebonised borders. The register plates and vernier are of ivory with three weather indications of 'Fair', 'Change' and 'Rain'. The squared hinged cistern cover contains a concertina cistern; these seem peculiar to Scotland and are formed by fixing a leather sleeve between the top and bottom halves of a boxwood cistern. There is no leather base but a portable screw can still be applied to the boxwood base of the cistern.

The maker was J. & J. Gardner of 43 Bell Street, Glasgow, around 1810. The senior partner was John Gardner who founded the business around 1770. In 1779 he advertised in the *Glasgow Mercury*:

Barometers constructed on the most improved principles, so as to admit of being carried to any distance with the greatest safety; likewise for measuring the heights of hills, which have a peculiar adjustment to

103

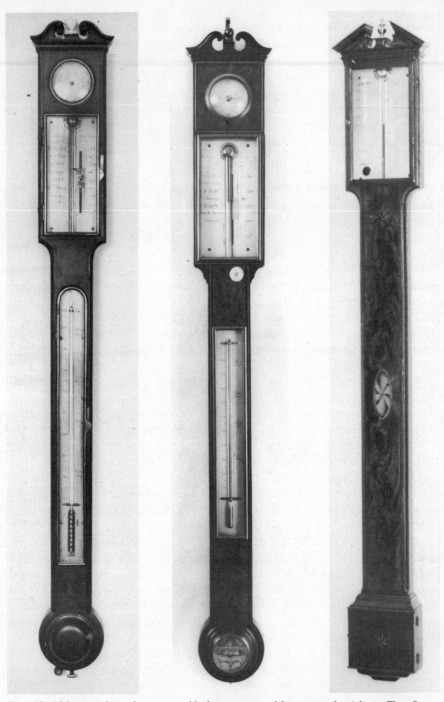

Fig. 130 Mahogany cistern barometer with thermometer and hygrometer by Adams, Fleet Street, London, c. 1810 (*Antony Preston Antiques Ltd, Stow-on-the-Wold*). *Fig.* 131 Mahogany cistern barometer with thermometer, hygrometer and spirit level by Rubergall, Coventry Street, London, c. 1810 (*Gerald Campbell, Lechlade*). *Fig.* 132 Mahogany bulb cistern barometer with marquetry decorations by Tarone, Bristol, c. 1810 (*J. & M. Bristow, Tetbury*).

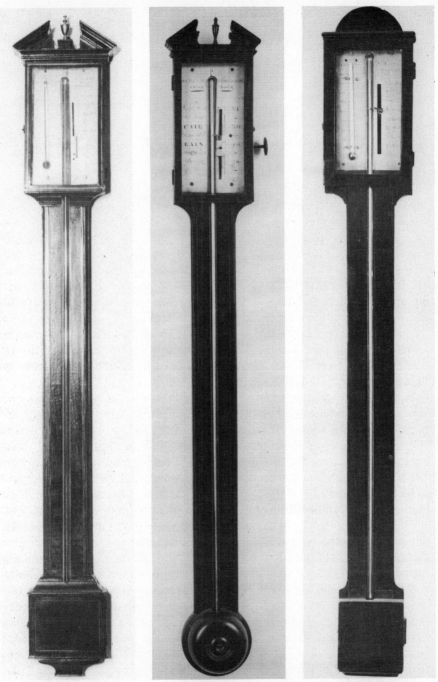

Fig. 133 Mahogany bulb cistern barometer with exposed tube and ebony and boxwood stringing by
P. Gally, Bristol, c. 1810 (*M. W. Cox, Bristol*).   *Fig.* 134 Mahogany bulb cistern barometer with
moulded edges, cross-banding and stringing. Hinged door and key to adjust the vernier by Josh. Pastoreli,
47 Alberon Street, Liverpool, c. 1810.   *Fig.* 135 Mahogany bulb cistern barometer with hinged doors
to silvered brass register plates and cistern. Sickle-shaped manual pointer by C. Zappa, Sheffield,
c. 1815.

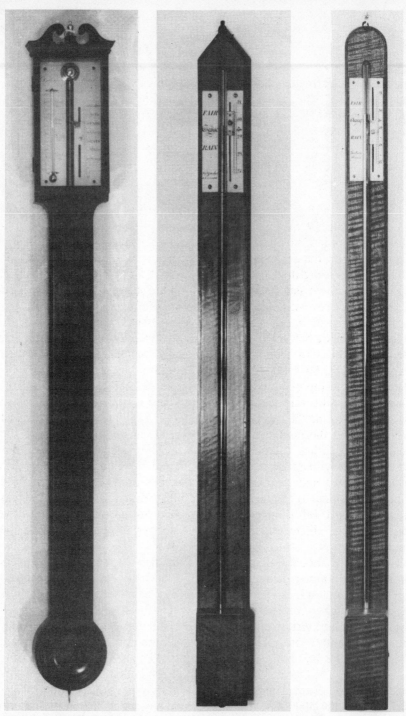

Fig. 136 Mahogany portable cistern barometer with scroll pediment and shallow turned cistern cover by Dollond, London, c. 1820 (*H. W. Keil Ltd, Broadway*). *Fig.* 137 Satinwood cistern barometer by J. & J. Gardner, Glasgow, c. 1810 (*M. W. Cox, Bristol*). *Fig.* 138 Satinwood cistern barometer by Gardners, Glasgow, c. 1822.

regulate the surface of the mercury in one place and have the mercury boiled in the tube.

The business continued in the name of a Gardner until the twentieth century as optical, mathematical or philosophical instrument-makers. A similar barometer was made by Gardners, Glasgow, in 1822 and is illustrated in *Fig.* 138. The satinwood veneer gives the effect of cross-banding between the moulded edges of the case and the illusion is extended to the hinged cistern cover which encloses a concertina cistern and portable screw. The register plates and vernier are of ivory and there are the three usual weather indications.

An inexpensive ordinary barometer is shown in *Fig.* 140 which was probably made for school or instructional use. The plain mahogany case is grooved to contain the tube which is held in place by a tapered rectangle of wood which slots into position below the centre of the case. The indicator housing is of brass, but the register plates are made of glazed cardboard. The tube has the same bore throughout its length so that a rise of half an inch in the mercury is shown as a rise of one inch on the scale, which is calibrated from 28 to 31 inches with divisions of one-tenth of an inch.

The hanging ring has a hand-made screw, which suggests that the barometer was made before 1851, whilst the indicator housing appears to be of late Georgian design. The initials T.N.P. are punched on the side of the case and these are, no doubt, the maker's initials.

A type of round-top pediment used during the second quarter of the nineteenth century is illustrated in *Fig.* 141. The case is of solid mahogany and as the glass protecting the register plates is fixed, a key is necessary to adjust the vernier. The thermometer is interesting because, in addition to the Fahrenheit scale, it has a Réaumur scale. In 1730 René A. F. de Réaumur suggested a scale with a freezing point of zero and a boiling point of 80°. The scale was adopted and named after him; it was used extensively on the Continent but is not often seen in the United Kingdom. The scale was occasionally used on thermometers attached to barometers from the beginning of the nineteenth century, but always as an addition to the Fahrenheit scale.

Bow-fronted mahogany barometers with urn-shaped cistern covers continued to be popular throughout the first half of the nineteenth century and an unusual example is shown in *Fig.* 144. The attractively slim case is veneered with highly grained mahogany and contrasts with the black raised edging and ebonised cistern cover, also the black vertical inlay on the sides of the cistern cover. Bow-fronted glass is used for the barometer and thermometer cases and both scales are signed 'Thomas Jones, 62 Charing Cross, London'. The barometer scale is not divided into tenths of an inch nor is there a vernier; instead, a circular scale to one-hundredth of an inch is engraved above the tube. The scale hand is moved simultaneously with the mercury level pointer by operating the key on the right-hand side of the case. The same accuracy is achieved as with a vernier.

Thomas Jones made this barometer around 1820. He was born in 1775 and

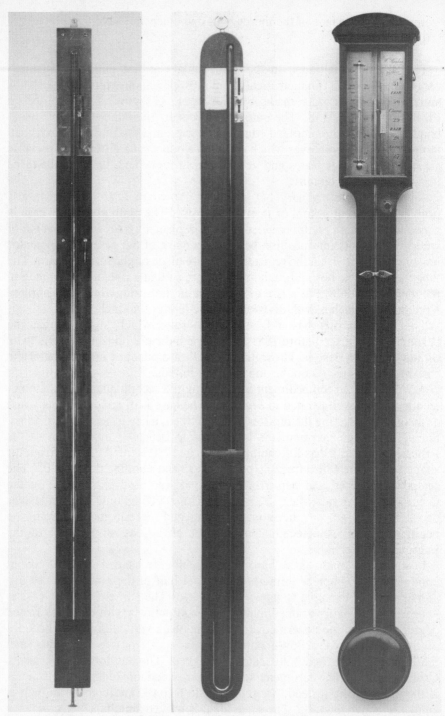

Fig. 139   Mahogany portable cistern barometer with silvered brass register plates, 37 inches high, by J. Dunn, Edinburgh, c. 1830 (*Sotheby's, London*).   *Fig.* 140   Ordinary mahogany siphon barometer. Unnamed, c. 1820.   *Fig.* 141   Mahogany bulb cistern barometer with thermometer having Fahrenheit and Réaumur scales by H. Hughes, 120 Fenchurch Street, London, c. 1825.

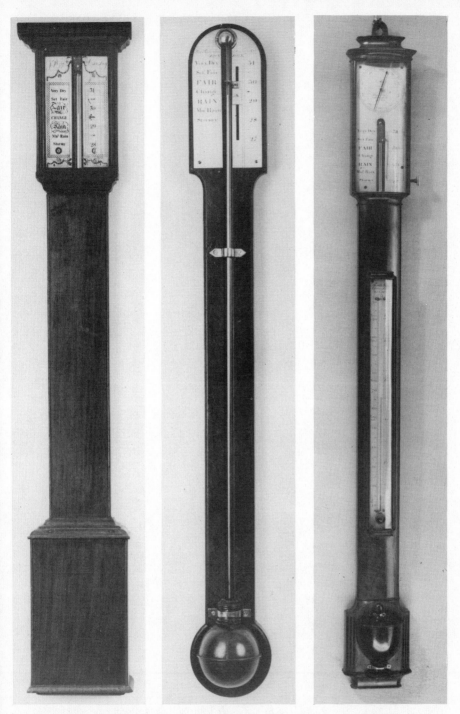

Fig. 142 Mahogany bulb cistern barometer in squared and moulded case by J. Pozzi, Oswestry, c. 1825.   *Fig.* 143 Mahogany bulb cistern barometer by Thomas Rubergall, 24 Coventry Street, London, c. 1825. At one time in the ownership of William Wordsworth.   *Fig.* 144 Mahogany bow-fronted cistern barometer by Thomas Jones, 62 Charing Cross, London, c. 1820 (*Hotspur Ltd, London*).

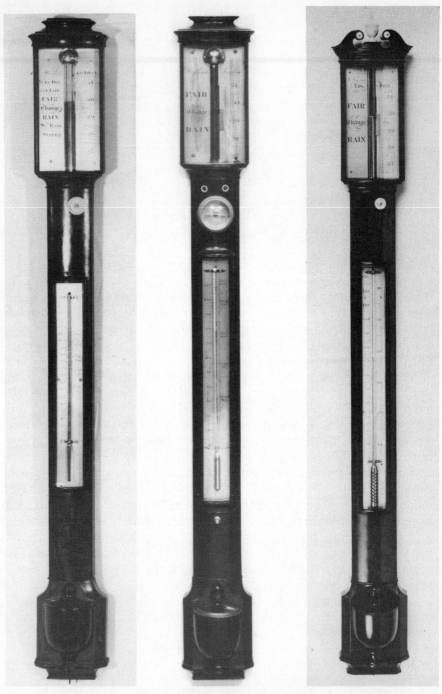

Fig. 145 Mahogany bow-fronted cistern barometer with flat moulded pediment and ebonised urn-shaped cistern cover with side diamond-shaped inlay by Hughes, London, c. 1820 (*M. W. Cox, Bristol*).
Fig. 146 Mahogany bow-fronted cistern barometer with thermometer and adjustable hygrometer by Dollond, London, c. 1830 (*Phillips, London*). *Fig.* 147 Mahogany bow-fronted barometer with scroll pediment by J. Newman, 122 Regent Street, London, c. 1830 (*Patric Capon, London*).

was apprenticed to Jesse Ramsden in 1789. He was in business on his own as an optical, mathematical and philosophical instrument-maker by 1806 and worked from various addresses until 1850. He was an authority on astronomical and meteorological instruments and made marine and mountain barometers.

A type of barometer that was invariably made with paper plates is shown in *Fig.* 148. The oak case is veneered with mahogany and the hemispherical bulb cistern cover is in two sections, which suggests that it was originally fitted with an open cistern. This type of instrument, which features paper plates and a simple arched case, was common on the Continent from early in the eighteenth century, but it did not become popular in England until the end of the century. The printed plates are decorated with trailing vines and protected by glass which is fixed flush against the plates. The maker was Adam Routledge of 32 English Street, Carlisle, who made clocks, watches and barometers between 1828 and 1858.

Charles Howorth of Halifax was a prolific maker of barometers with paper plates during the second quarter of the nineteenth century. He made the bulb cistern instrument shown in *Figs.* 149 and 150. The case is of solid mahogany with the glazed door cross-banded in mahogany with an ebonised border. There is a moulded cornice with fretted pediment and the cistern cover has a marquetry decoration.

A similar barometer by Howorth is illustrated in *Fig.* 151. The shape and decoration of the case are different but the overall effect is the same. A different style of paper plate is used; it has no winter weather indications, and a paper scale for the Fahrenheit thermometer has been stuck over the right-hand edge of the register plate. There is no attempt at accuracy with only brass pointers for the two scales which are operated manually on brass rods. The paper plates are decorated with acorn and vine scrolls topped by masonic signs.

Identical paper plates were used by Samuel Lainton, also of Halifax, on the barometer illustrated in *Fig.* 152. The rosewood case is cross-banded with satinwood. Carved scroll mounts support the barometer housing which is surmounted by a scroll pediment. Charles Howorth and Samuel Lainton also made similar angle barometers with identical paper plates which suggests that they both obtained their supplies from the same source. An alternative could be that one of them made all the instruments and sold some of them to the other.

George Purcheon of Glass House, Leeds, made barometers with paper, painted and enamelled plates around 1830 and two are illustrated. *Figs.* 153 and 154 show a bulb cistern barometer in a pine case veneered with mahogany and having marquetry decoration. A glazed door protects the printed paper plates which are signed G. Purcheon, Leeds, Glass House, in a cartouche below the scroll adornment.

Figs. 155 and 156 illustrate a similar bulb cistern barometer in a pine case veneered with mahogany and having a more elaborate marquetry ornamentation. There are fretwork scrolls to the hood and also a fretwork pediment. The register plates are painted and decorated with flower sprays coloured

111

 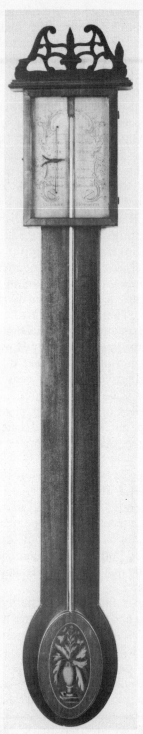

Fig. 148   Mahogany bulb cistern barometer with paper plates by A. Routledge, Carlisle, c. 1830.
Fig. 149   Mahogany bulb cistern barometer with paper plates by Charles Howorth, c. 1830.

112

Fig. 150   Detail of *Fig.* 149.

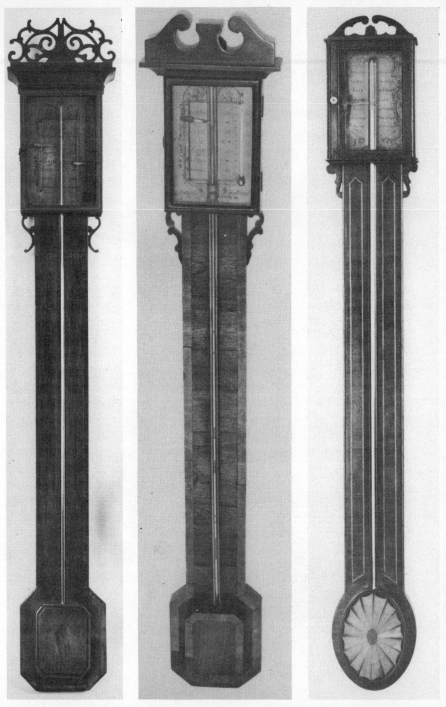

Fig. 151 Mahogany bulb cistern barometer with thermometer. Paper plates by Charles Howorth, Halifax, c. 1830 (*Lalonde Bros & Parham, Bristol*).   *Fig.* 152   Rosewood bulb cistern barometer with thermometer. Paper plates by Samuel Lainton, Halifax, c. 1830 (*Phillips, London*).   *Fig.* 153 Mahogany bulb cistern barometer with paper plates by G. Purcheon, Leeds, Glass House, c. 1830.

114

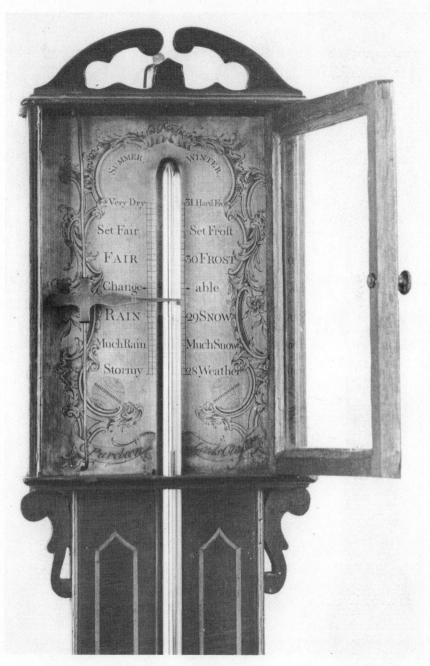

Fig. 154   Detail of *Fig.* 153.

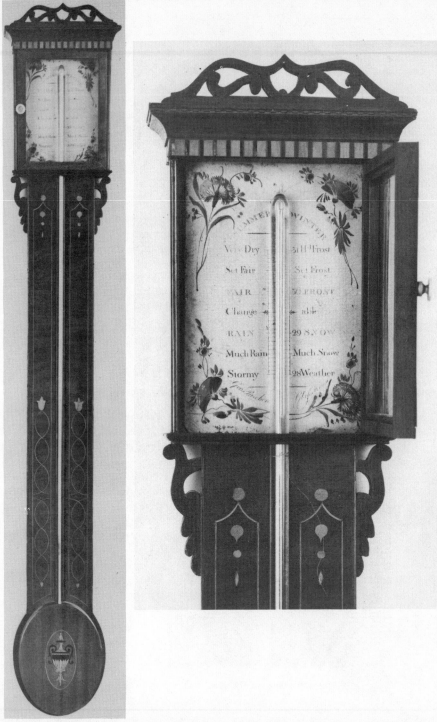

Fig. 155 Mahogany bulb cistern barometer with painted plates by Geo. Purchon, Glass House, c. 1830. *Fig.* 156 Detail of *Fig.* 155.

116

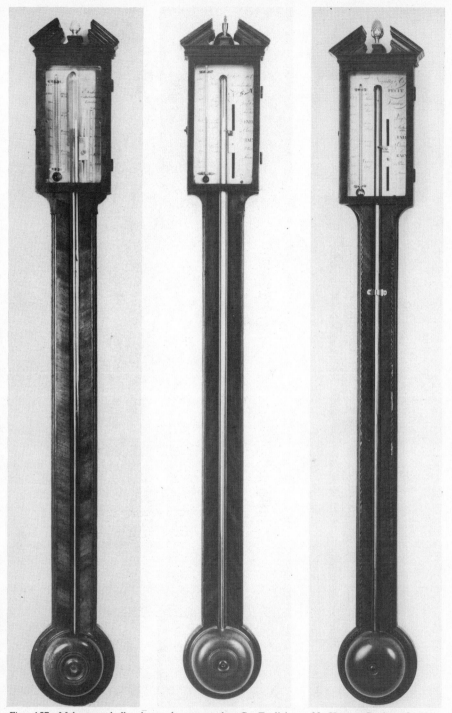

Fig. 157 Mahogany bulb cistern barometer by C. Tagliabue, 23 Hatton Garden, London, c. 1830. *Fig.* 158 Mahogany bulb cistern barometer by Josh. Peduzzy & Co., Manchester, c. 1830. *Fig.* 159 Mahogany bulb cistern barometer with chequered stringing by Negretty & Co., London, c. 1830.

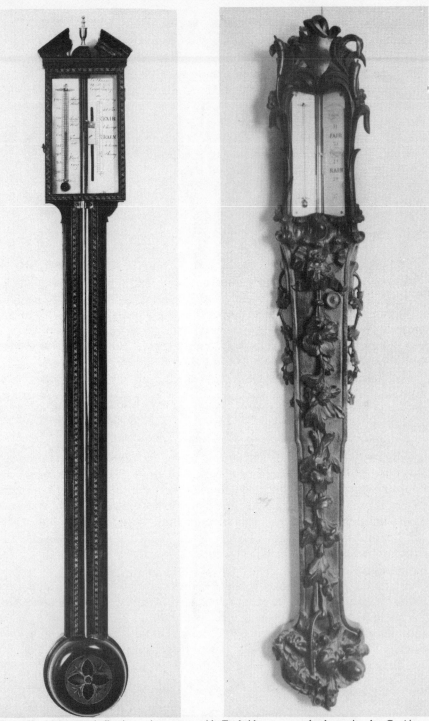

Fig. 160 Mahogany bulb cistern barometer with Tunbridge ware style decoration by C. Aiano, Northgate, Canterbury, c. 1830.   *Fig.* 161 Heavily carved mahogany cistern barometer by Watkins & Hill, 5 Charing Cross, London, c. 1835.

blue, brown, green, pink and red. It is signed 'Geo. Purchon, Glass House', but no doubt it is the same maker as G. Purcheon.

By far the most popular stick barometer produced in the second quarter of the nineteeth century was the broken pediment type illustrated in *Fig.* 157. The pine frame is veneered with mahogany giving a herring-bone pattern, with boxwood stringing along the moulded edges. The shallow turned cistern cover contains a bulb cistern tube, and the hinged and glazed door protects the silvered brass register plates and Fahrenheit thermometer. The seven weather indications are standard and the scale is from 27 to 31 inches, although the vernier cannot be used below 28 inches.

The maker was Caesar Tagliabue, an Italian immigrant, who was an optician and barometer-maker. He traded from various addresses in London between 1807 and 1846; the address engraved on the register plates is '23 Hatton Garden, London' where he was operating from 1829 to 1846. In 1837 his eldest daughter married his apprentice, Louis Casella, whom he took into partnership in 1838. The firm flourished and still trades today as scientific instrument-makers under the name of C. F. Casella & Co. Ltd.

A similar barometer of exceptional quality is shown in *Fig.* 160. The case is again veneered with mahogany, to give a feathered pattern, and for additional adornment there is ebony and boxwood stringing which borders an intricate chequered inlay in the style of Tunbridge ware. The same design is used on the glazed door whilst the shallow turned cistern cover is inlayed with different coloured woods to form leaves and a flower head.

The maker's name 'C. Aiano, North Gate, Canterbury' is engraved on the register plates. As already mentioned, he was an Italian immigrant who produced decorative barometers, clocks and thermometers between 1800 and 1840.

A unique mahogany barometer is illustrated in *Fig.* 161. The case is heavily carved with ribbons and trailing leaves and flowers whilst the cistern cover is carved in the shape of a basket of fruit. The register plates are flanked by bullrushes with a pediment in the form of a shield. A portable cistern is used and the key below the plates to set the vernier is also used to adjust the portable cistern. The silvered brass register plates have three weather indications, 'Fair, Change, Rain', which was common practice from around 1835. There is a mercury thermometer with Fahrenheit and Réaumur scales.

The barometer was probably made to order around 1835 by Watkins and Hill, 5 Charing Cross, London, which is engraved on the plates. This partnership, which was formed in 1819, made a number of unusual barometers. Jeremiah Watkins, the senior partner, was the nephew of Francis Watkins who made the calendar barometer illustrated in *Fig.* 89. The firm was absorbed by Elliott Brothers in 1856.

6

Victorian, 1837–1901

A number of changes took place in the design of the stick barometer during the early Victorian period. The broken and scroll or swan-neck pediments were displaced, in the main, by square moulded or round tops, and silvered brass register plates and thermometer scales were superseded, over a period, by ivory register plates and thermometer scales.

The bow-fronted design was still used and *Figs.* 162 and 163 illustrate a popular type of cistern barometer made around 1840. The case is of solid mahogany and the bow front highlights the attractive grain in the wood. Ebonised stringing applied to the edges of the case matches the black urn-shaped cistern cover. Both barometer and thermometer have ivory register plates within fixed bow-fronted glass cases. The thermometer has a Fahrenheit and a Réaumur scale.

There are only three weather indications, Fair, Change and Rain, which is common for this type of barometer. The detail in *Fig.* 163 shows the changes in the style of engraving which took place during the early Victorian period. A gradual change to a Gothic style of lettering was seen with 'Change' being engraved as shown. Broad Roman serif capitals were used for 'Fair' and 'Rain', but the previously applied Roman capitals and lower case continued to be used for the rest of the register plate lettering. By the third quarter of the nineteenth century Roman sans serif capitals were being used.

The barometer in *Fig.* 165 has ivory barometer and thermometer scales, but it is unusual because it has an ebonised urn-shaped cistern cover with a flat-fronted mahogany case. Another interesting feature is the gadrooning on the pediment above the moulded cornice. The thermometer has Fahrenheit and Réaumur scales and the complete thermometer box can be removed by pressing the ivory knob below the box. There are two sets of weather indications, two verniers and two ivory keys, below the plates, to adjust them. Above the weather indications there is engraved '10 a.m. yesterday' on the left-hand plate and '10 a.m. today' on the right-hand plate; with the two verniers it was intended to read the barometer daily at 10 a.m. so that day-to-day comparisons could be made.

The barometer is signed 'Bate, London'. This is probably Robert Brettel Bate who was a mathematical instrument-maker and a member of the Clockmakers' Company. His business was in Cheapside, London, where he was active between 1807 and 1849.

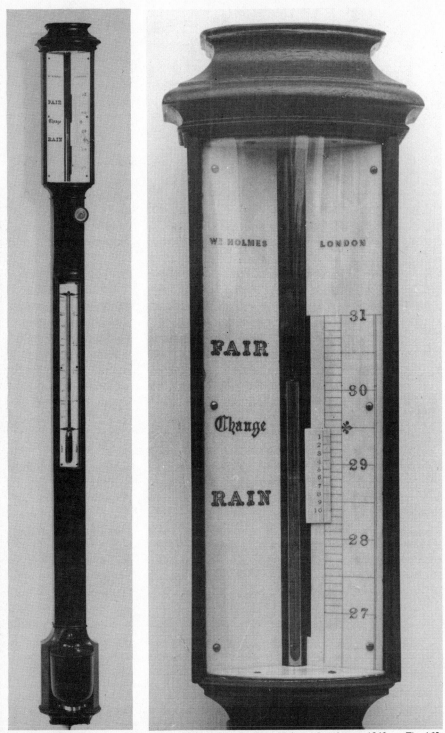

Fig. 162   Mahogany cistern barometer with bow-front by Wm. Holmes, London, c. 1840.   *Fig*. 163 Detail of *Fig*. 162.

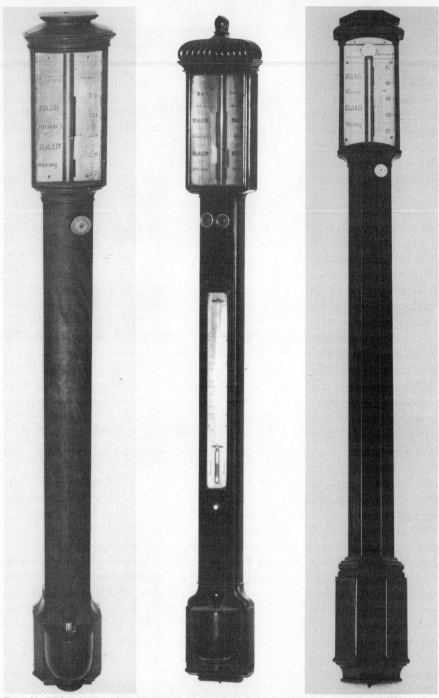

Fig. 164 Mahogany bow-fronted cistern barometer with ivory register plates and ivory floating gauge by P. Squire, Chemist to the Queen, 277 Oxford Street, London, c. 1840 (*Phillips, London*).   *Fig.* 165 Mahogany cistern barometer by Bate, London, c. 1845 (*Phillips, London*).   *Fig.* 166 Rosewood cistern barometer in pentagonal case by Marratt, King William Street, London Bridge, c. 1850 (*Richard Cookson, Leominster*).

Fig. 166 illustrates another unusual barometer made by Marratt, King William Street, London Bridge, around 1850. The case is in rosewood and the trunk and cistern cover are pentagonal with boxwood stringing on all the corners. A fixed bow glass covers the ivory register plates and the vernier is adjusted by the ivory key on the trunk; this is also used to adjust the portable screw to the boxwood cistern.

John Marratt was an optical, mathematical and philosophical instrument-maker in London between 1833 and 1859. His address was 63 King William Street between 1845 and 1859 when he formed a partnership known as Marratt and Short.

An example of a round-top barometer can be seen in *Fig.* 168. The case is veneered with mahogany to give a feathered effect and the tube is protected by a mahogany sheath. The glazed door to the ivory register plates is also veneered and, surprisingly, a hemispherical cistern cover is used with a bulb cistern tube. The plates are signed 'Thos. Jones, 62 Charing Cross'; he was the notable instrument-maker who made the barometer illustrated in *Fig.* 144.

In the 1850s Negretti & Zambra were offering a wide choice of stick or pediment barometers, as they were then called, for domestic use. The cases were made of mahogany, rosewood, ebony, oak or walnut, and could be obtained in either plain designs or 'handsomely and elaborately carved and embellished, in a variety of designs suitable for private homes, large halls or public buildings'. The register plates and thermometer scales could be of ivory, porcelain or silvered brass. Two verniers could be fitted and two sets of weather indications could be engraved, one on each side of the mercury tube, so that one vernier could register the last reading and so show at a glance the extent of the rise or fall in the interval. The cheap instruments had open faces and plain frames with a sliding vernier instead of a rack-and-pinion mechanism, whilst the most expensive types had the benefit of plate glass to protect the register plates and thermometer. In addition, barometers could be made to specific requirements.

The types of barometers advertised by Negretti & Zambra in the 1850s were made until late in the nineteenth century so that it is difficult to date individual instruments with any accuracy.

A further difficulty in dating barometers from this period comes from the common practice among makers of engraving the retailer's name and address on the register plates rather than their own. This was at the request of retailers who considered that their own standing and reputation would be enhanced if the impression was given that they were the makers. In some instances the maker would engrave his name on the barometer but put the address or town of the retailer. It is also thought that some Italian makers, who were wholesalers, would engrave their own names on the barometers but add the town or address of the retailer. This was certainly the practice of some clockmakers and it could account for the very large number of Italians who, on the face of it, appear to have been living in small towns up and down the country.

However, it is sometimes possible to establish the name of the maker by

123

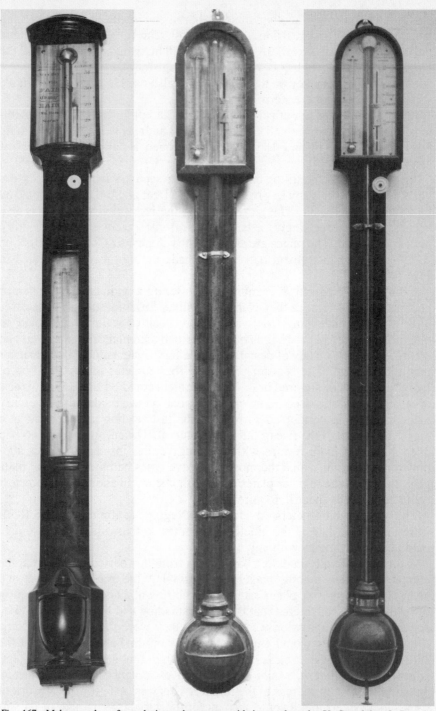

Fig. 167 Mahogany bow-fronted cistern barometer with ivory plates by V. Somalvico & Son, 14 Charles Street, Hatton Garden, London, c. 1850. *Fig.* 168 Mahogany bulb cistern barometer by Thos. Jones, 62 Charing Cross, c. 1850 (*Christies, London*). *Fig.* 169 Rosewood cistern barometer by Negretti & Zambra, c. 1850.

looking at the back of the case to see if there are any operating instructions. Some considerate makers made a point of pasting instructions for setting up the barometer on the back of the frame and added their name and address.

The barometer in *Fig.* 169 was made by Negretti & Zambra but the retailer's name 'W. Lund, 23 & 24 Fleet Street, London', is engraved on the register plates. The following printed 'Instructions for the Barometer' by Negretti & Zambra are pasted on the back of the case:

Suspend the Barometer on a hook or stout nail preferably with a round head. Insert the key (found just below the scales) to the square brass pin at the lower end of the instrument, turn gently towards the left hand till the screw stops. Then remove the key and return it for use near the scales as it was before. The cistern bottom being thus let down, the mercury will quickly sink to its proper level.

In removing the Barometer it is necessary to slope it gradually till the mercury has risen to the top of the tube, and then with the instrument reversed, to screw up the cistern by means of the key, use gently till it stops. It will then be portable with the lower end uppermost or lying flat, but it must not be jarred or receive a concussion.

The square brass pin, referred to in the instructions, has been replaced by a hand-adjustable screw making the use of the key unnecessary. The case is veneered with rosewood and has the then popular round-top hood.

The Negretti & Zambra partnership was formed in 1850 by Enrico (Henry) Negretti and Joseph Zambra as makers of scientific instruments. It expanded rapidly and still trades today specialising in instrumentation and control systems under the name of Negretti Automation in Aylesbury.

Rosewood appears to have been the most popular wood for making barometers during a limited period around the middle of the nineteenth century, and *Fig.* 170 shows another rosewood instrument which is typical of the time. The cistern tube is housed in a panelled case and the layout of the ivory register plates is identical to the last barometer except that they are set aslant. This arrangement was adopted when making the narrow marine barometers, at the beginning of the century, in order to gain width across the plates without widening the hood. From about 1840 the practice became common on domestic barometers, where the plates were protected by glass.

The name engraved on the register plates is 'W. & T. C. Heath, Devonport'. William and Thomas Heath are recorded as trading as opticians and barometer-makers at 46 Fore Street, Devonport between 1850 and 1852.

During the second half of the nineteenth century oak became increasingly popular, and solid oak cases were used extensively after 1870. The solid oak framed barometer in *Fig.* 172 is particularly interesting because it has porcelain register plates which are seldom found on extant barometers. The brass reading indicator in the form of two joined rings is unusual, as is the shape of the cistern cover.

The barometer can be dated about 1860 and was made by Elliott Bros of 449 Strand, London. The brothers were Charles and Frederick, the sons of

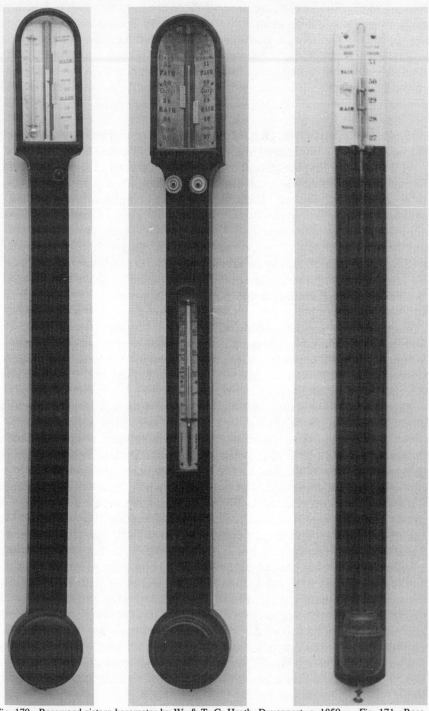

Fig. 170   Rosewood cistern barometer by W. & T. C. Heath, Devonport, c. 1850.   *Fig.* 171   Rose-wood cistern barometer with two sets of weather indications and two verniers by Webb, Taunton, c. 1860.   *Fig.* 172   Oak cistern barometer with porcelain register plates by Elliott Bros, 449 Strand, London, c. 1860.

William who, as a young man in 1795, was apprenticed to one William Backwell, a London maker of compasses and drawing instruments. The indenture is of interest as it throws light on the considerable control the master exercised over his apprentice at that time. The following is an extract:

He shall not commit fornication nor contract matrimony within the said term. He shall not play cards or dice tables or any other unlawful games whereby his master may have loss with his goods or otherwise, he shall neither buy nor sell, he shall not haunt taverns or playhouses nor absent himself from his master's service day or night unlawfully but in all things as a faithful apprentice he shall behave himself towards his said master and all during the said term . . .

In return for this abdication of most of a young man's pleasures, the master promised:

To find, provide and allow the said apprentice, competent and sufficient meat, drink, apparel, lodging, washing and other things necessary and fit for an apprentice.

Owing to the death of his master, William Elliott was unable to complete his seven years' apprenticeship and in 1800 he started in business on his own making drawing instruments. He soon diversified and in 1816, it is recorded, he made a magic lantern for the Duchess of Wellington for which he charged 34s. The sons were taken into partnership in 1830, and in 1857 the partnership took over the business of Watkins & Hill. Elliott Bros are now part of the GEC–Elliott Automation Group.

By the middle of the nineteenth century there were a very large number of barometer-makers and competition was very keen. Factory methods were used for their production and in an endeavour to increase sales some makers began to make barometers for specific purposes.

In 1857 an agricultural, gardener's or cottage barometer was marketed by L. Casella and one is shown in *Fig.* 173. It was expressly designed as a cheap, light and portable barometer for use in cottages, garden sheds, greenhouses and farm buildings. It is made of solid mahogany with printed paper plates protected by glass. The standard weather indications are used and below them is the word 'Compensating'. This indicates that the inch calibrations on the register plates are, in fact, slightly less than inches, to compensate for the slight rise or fall in the level of the mercury in the bulb cistern, as the height of the mercury ranges between 26 and 31 inches on the scale.

It can be confidently stated that this type of barometer was introduced in 1857, as *The Field* of 7 November 1857 commented:

Casella's cottage barometer has lately been brought under our notice, very much to our delight and profit. They have registered with unerring faithfulness the recent changes in the weather.

In the *Cottage Gardener* of 27 October 1857 the following testimonial was written:

. . .would adorn alike the gardener's cottage or the hall of the mansion. We are much obliged to Mr. Casella for thus popularizing these useful instruments. His name is a guarantee for the character of any instrument.

The following printed 'Instructions and Remarks' on the back of the barometer are still legible and worth repeating:

In placing the Agricultural Barometer a shaded position is the best. The words Rain, Change, Fair, etc. are of less moment than the Figures; thus 29½, or Change, is considered about the Mean or Point leading to a change of weather and a rise in the mercury to ½ an inch above this point, or a fall of a ¼ of an inch below, is generally succeeded by decidedly Dry or Wet weather. In this country the mercury seldom rises higher than 30½ inches, or falls below 28. A gradual Rise or Fall of the mercury, indicates greater change than sudden fluctuations. Where the state of the weather appears to disagree with any great change of the barometer, such change may be looked for with double force with no great distance off. Thus, in May 1857, in and around London, the mercury which had been lowering for some days, began to rise with but ¾ of an inch of rain, whilst Reading, in Berkshire, only thirty miles off, was visited by a storm so severe as almost to form an event in the annals of the town.

The following remarks of the learned Dr. Halley ('Philosophical Transactions' No. 187) will be found useful and interesting: 1st. In calm weather, when the air is inclined to rain the mercury is commonly low. 2nd. It is generally high in good, serene, settled fair weather. 3rd. It sinks lowest of all in very great winds, though not attended with rain. 4th. The greatest height of the mercury is observed when an easterly or northerly wind prevails. 5th. In calm frosty weather, the mercury is generally high. 6th. After very great storms of wind, when the mercury has been low, it usually rises again very fast. 7th. More northerly places have a greater alteration of the rise and fall of the mercury than the more southerly. 8th. Within the tropics, and near them, the changes and alterations in the weather make little or no variation in the height of the mercury. For instance, at Naples, it hardly ever exceeds an inch; whereas at Upminster, Dr. Dereham informs us, there is a difference of two and a half inches and at Petersburgh 3.31 inches.

The words 'Agricultural Barometer' are printed above the maker's name 'L. Casella, London'. He was mentioned earlier in connection with the stick barometer by C. Tagliabue shown in *Fig.* 157. He married Tagliabue's eldest daughter in 1837 and was taken into partnership a year later. The firm

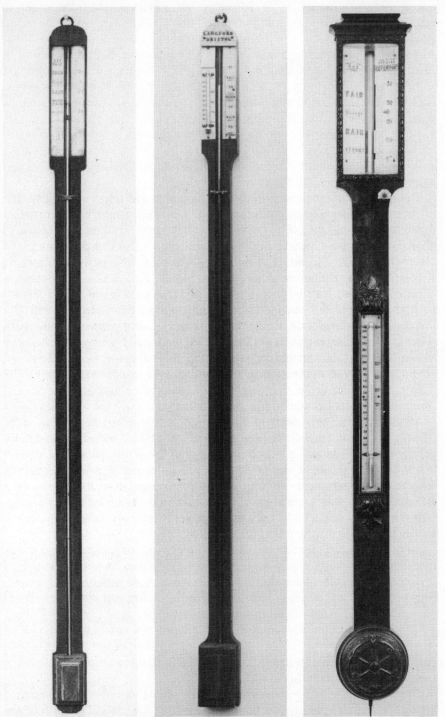

Fig. 173 Agricultural or cottage mahogany barometer by L. Casella, London, c. 1860.   *Fig.* 174
Cottage oak barometer by Langford, Bristol, c. 1865.   *Fig.* 175 Mahogany cistern barometer by Cox,
Devonport, c. 1860.

129

traded as Louis Casella & Co. between 1848 and 1860 and were scientific instrument-makers to the Admiralty, the Board of Trade, America, India, Russia, etc.

A country-made cottage barometer by Langford of Bristol is shown in *Fig.* 174. The case is of solid oak and the shape suggests that it was copied from the Casella barometer. Langford probably read the 'Instructions' on the back of Casella's barometer — particularly the suggested maximum variations in pressure in England — because he limited his scale from 27½ inches to 31 inches. The register and name plates are of ivory and the thermometer has a Fahrenheit scale.

William Langford is recorded as having worked in Bristol as a watch- and clockmaker between 1825 and 1870.

The Great Exhibition at the Crystal Palace in 1851 had a considerable effect on furniture design; as far as barometers were concerned there was a move towards using solid wood rather than veneers, and carving began to appear on the cases. Sixteen instrument-makers exhibited at the Exhibition: George Dollond, Elliott & Sons, J. S. Marratt, Negretti & Zambra, J. Newman, M. Pillischer, Andrew Ross, Somalvico & Co., Carpenter & Westley, Chadburn Bros, E. J. Dent, C. W. Dixey, William Harris & Son, F. A. Pizzala, Watkins and Hill, and the Frenchman Eugene Bourdon.

A cistern barometer in a pine frame veneered with mahogany and with some carving is shown in *Fig.* 175. The glazed ivory register plate housing has an egg-and-dart moulding, whilst the thermometer case and cistern cover have carved decoration in the form of leaf and flower scrolls. The maker was William Charles Cox of Devonport who was an optician and instrument-maker between 1822 and 1860.

Another carved barometer in a rosewood case is illustrated in *Fig.* 176. The pediment has two carved scrolls surmounted by a flower head and there are reverse scrolls below the cistern box which is glazed with a carved surround. The glazed frame to the duplicate ivory register plates is carved with an egg-and-tongue motif. The thermometer has Fahrenheit and Réaumur scales with a spiral reservoir. An unusual feature is the Gay-Lussac type tube which is normally only found on scientific barometers. The plates are signed H. Field & Son, Birmingham.

An oat-beard hygrometer has only a very limited effective life and it was considered that the farmer, who needed more than most people to be able to forecast the weather accurately, should have a more accurate instrument. This took the form of a wet and dry bulb hygrometer and these were fitted to farmer's barometers from the early 1860s.

Negretti & Zambra were early makers of farmer's barometers and one by them is shown in *Figs.* 177 and 178. It has a portable cistern tube in a solid oak case and there is a sliding vernier. Admiral Fitzroy's weather indications are used on the porcelain register plates.

The wet and dry bulb hygrometer comprises two Fahrenheit thermometers set on the register plates, one being each side of the tube. The bulb of the thermometer on the left-hand plate is exposed and records the temperature of the surrounding air. The bulb of the thermometer on the right-hand plate is

130

covered with a piece of muslin which is attached to some lamp-wick cotton, the ends of which are immersed in water in a small glass container fixed just below the thermometer. The water rises to the muslin by capillary action and keeps the thermometer bulb moist. The humidity of the air is obtained by taking a reading from each thermometer and noting the difference between them. The wet bulb thermometer will always be found to give a lower reading than the dry bulb thermometer and the greater the difference between them the less the amount of moisture in the air.

The evaporation of the water in the muslin round the bulb is a continuous process and this causes the temperature of the muslin to fall below that of the surrounding air. As the muslin is in contact with the thermometer bulb it will, of course, lower its temperature. A difference of 5 to 8 degrees was considered to indicate a healthy amount of moisture in the air of a living-room.

For the hygrometer to work efficiently it is essential for the barometer to be set up in a position sufficiently exposed to the external air. If, for any reason, this was not practicable, a separate hygrometer could be purchased. Some time later a set of tables was produced giving the value of hygrometric readings in a simple form for use by the ordinary observer.

George Adams realised the usefulness of the hygrometer to farmers. In 1790, in his 'Short Dissertation on the Barometer', he quoted a Mr Marshall in his minutes of agriculture:

Yesterday morning while the hygrometer stood at 2 degrees moist, the peas were by no means fit for carrying; the halm was green and the peas soft. About 10 o'clock the hygrometer fell to 1 degree dry: before one the peas were in good order. I went up into the field, merely on the WORD of the hygrometer, and found the peas fit to be carried. It is plain therefore, that on a scattered farm, in hay-time and harvest, a hygrometer, must be peculiarly useful.

Similar farmer's barometers were made for about fifty years; they all appear to have had oak frames, but some were more elaborate than the one described, having carved oak frames and ornamental mountings. The register plates were often made of ivory.

Barometers made specifically for miners, called miner's or pit barometers, were on sale certainly before 1864, but it was not until 1872 that an Act of Parliament was passed making the use of a barometer compulsory. Accurate records were maintained from the barometers previously in use and it was shown that before an explosion in a coal mine there was a diminution of atmospheric pressure. The government of the day was so convinced of the advantages of using a barometer in mines that when passing the Mines (Coal) Regulations Act 1872, 'An Act to consolidate and amend the Acts relating to the Regulation of Coal Mines and certain other Mines', the following Section 26 was included: 'After dangerous gas has been found in any mine, a barometer and thermometer shall be placed above ground in a conspicuous position near the entrance to the mine.'

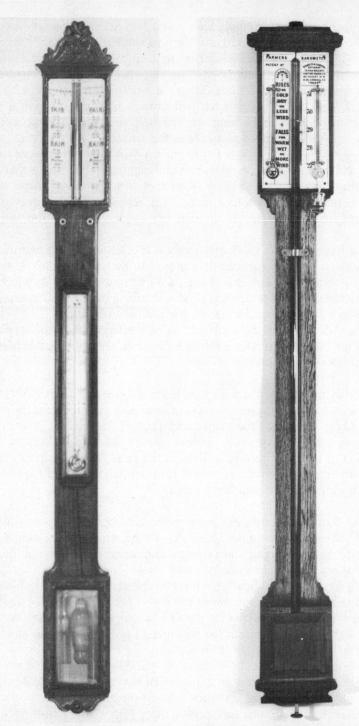

Fig. 176   Rosewood Gay-Lussac cistern barometer by H. Field & Son, Birmingham, c. 1860 (*M. & S. Cumper Ltd, South Newton*).   *Fig.* 177   Farmer's oak barometer with wet and dry bulb hygrometer by Negretti & Zambra, London, c. 1865.

132

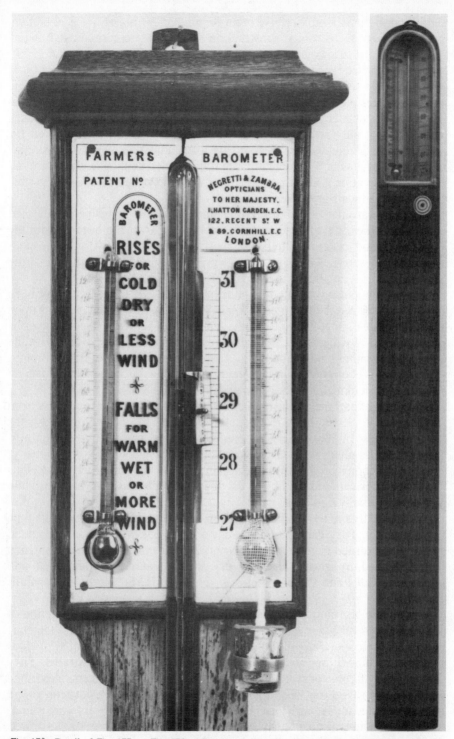

Fig. 178 Detail of Fig. 177.   Fig. 179 Miner's oak barometer by J. Davis & Son of London and Derby, c. 1875.

Although the Act only referred to a barometer for use above ground they were, in fact, all of robust construction so that they could be used underground. All the instruments made were of a very similar design and *Fig.* 179 shows a standard type by J. Davis & Son of London and Derby made around 1875. It has a solid oak frame with a glass face framed in bronze metal. The aslant register plates are of ivory and are calibrated from 26 to 33 inches to allow the barometer to be used at least 2,000 feet below sea level. A cistern tube is used and for accuracy the scale is compensated or corrected for capacity. A single vernier is fitted with an adjusting key. The mercury thermometer has a Fahrenheit scale but, understandably, there are no weather indications on the register plates, as the prime object was to give warning of low air pressures.

Some pit barometers had metal or enamel plates and some were calibrated up to 34 inches. Others had an india-rubber bag over the cistern, with the brasswork and cistern coated with marine glue to prevent moisture penetrating. These types of barometers were made until 1930 with very little alteration.

The most popular type of cheap stick barometer ever made must have been the model barometer illustrated in *Fig.* 180. It is made of solid oak with open register plates, but the bulb of the Fahrenheit mercury thermometer is protected by a wide brass loop. The register plates are of ivory with the standard weather indications and there is an ivory vernier. 'Hanny, Shrewsbury' is engraved on the plates and he was probably James Hanny who was a clockmaker in Shrewsbury between 1835 and 1879.

This type of barometer must have been sold for a period of fifty years from about 1860 to 1910. In 1875 the sale price was 13s 6d with 3s extra for enamel plates. In 1885 the price, with ivory plates, had risen to one guinea. Silvered brass plates were also offered and the case could be of mahogany, rosewood, ebony or walnut, either plain or carved, in a variety of designs suitable for private rooms, large halls or public buildings. The best design in walnut cost twelve guineas.

An alternative to the model barometer, but more expensive, was the type shown in *Fig.* 182. The panelled case is of solid oak with a square moulded top and flat turned cistern cover. Ivory is used for both sets of scales which are protected by glass. The mercury thermometer has Fahrenheit and Réaumur scales and the barometer is signed J. H. Steward, 54 Cornhill, London.

During the last quarter of the nineteenth century a very large selection of stick or pediment barometers was available. A catalogue issued by James J. Hicks of 8 Hatton Garden, London, in 1875 gave the prices of forty-four different pediment barometers of which twenty-one were illustrated. They were mainly large, carved, solid oak instruments with pediments described variously as shield top, shield and point, pointed top, ecclesiastical, round top, castellated top, square top and dome top. The cistern covers were round, square or rectangular and heavily carved.

Three of the barometers illustrated in the catalogue are shown in *Fig.* 183 and they were described as follows:

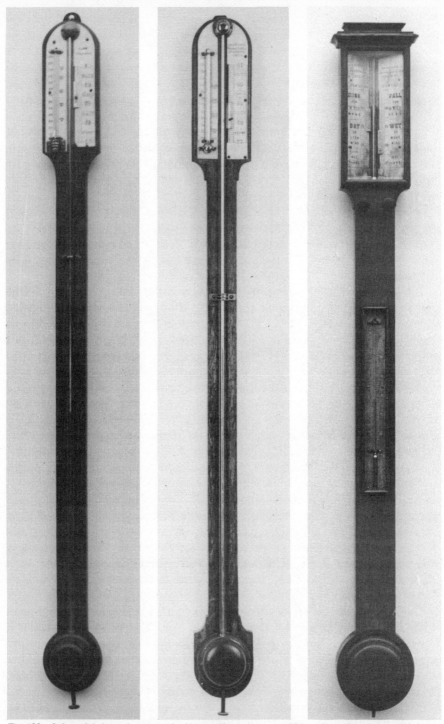

Fig. 180 Oak model cistern barometer by Hanny, Shrewsbury, c. 1875. *Fig.* 181 Oak model cistern barometer by J. H. Steward, 54 Cornhill, London, c. 1875. *Fig.* 182 Oak cistern barometer by J. H. Steward, 54 Cornhill, London, c. 1875.

135

Fig. 183 Three carved oak pediment barometers from the catalogue of James J. Hicks, 8 Hatton Garden, London, c. 1875.

Left-hand barometer
Large Carved Solid Oak Barometer, double vernier with metal pointers, rack and pinion adjustments, enamelled or ivory scales, attached thermometer and floating gauge. £5 10/-.

Centre barometer
Torricelli–Drebel Barometer (Registered). The frame of this instrument is elaborately carved in the Italian Renaissance style, and is surmounted by a carved head of Torricelli, under which are the words in antique letter, 'Torricelli invt. 1643'. A highly sensitive spiral Thermometer is attached, with Fahrenheit and Celsius Scales, and surmounted by a carved head of Drebel, the inventor of the Thermometer, with words also in antique letter, 'Drebel invt. 1620' under the head. In addition to being a handsome piece of furniture for the hall or library, the instrument thus assumes an educational character. It has a bold tube supported by enamel scales, having Fitzroy words and double vernier of enamelled glass, with rack and pinion adjustments and portable screw. £7 10/-.

Right-hand barometer
Best Carved Solid Oak Barometer, carved cross, enamelled or ivory scales, double vernier with metal pointers, rack and pinion adjustments and attached Thermometer. £4 10/-.

These three barometers show the Gothic influence on furniture design during the last quarter of the nineteenth century. There was an attempt by the Victorians to capture the spirit of the Middle Ages by the use of straight lines, solid wood rather than veneers and obtrusive carving.

Fig. 185 illustrates a solid oak cistern barometer made or retailed by B. Boese of Kidderminster, who was a clockmaker there between 1868 and 1876. The carving is obviously influenced by the Gothic ecclesiastical period. The ivory register plates are not protected by glass, but the spirit thermometer, which has Fahrenheit and Réaumur scales, has its bulb covered by a brass grille.

During the second half of the nineteenth century the aneroid barometer was becoming increasingly popular at the expense of the mercury instrument, but stick or pediment barometers were still made in small numbers until about 1905 when they were eventually displaced by the less expensive, more compact and thoroughly portable aneroid barometer.

Towards the end of the century few new barometer case designs appeared and those that were made were based on the design of earlier cases. An example is given in *Fig.* 186 made by Negretti & Zambra at the turn of the century. It is almost a reproduction of the bow-fronted urn cistern types made a hundred years earlier. The case is of mahogany and lined with boxwood, whilst the bow front is inlaid with foliate scrolls with fan ovals on the cistern cover. The moulded and flat cornice was used in the eighteenth century and the silvered brass register plates have Roman-type lettering. The height is 37 inches overall.

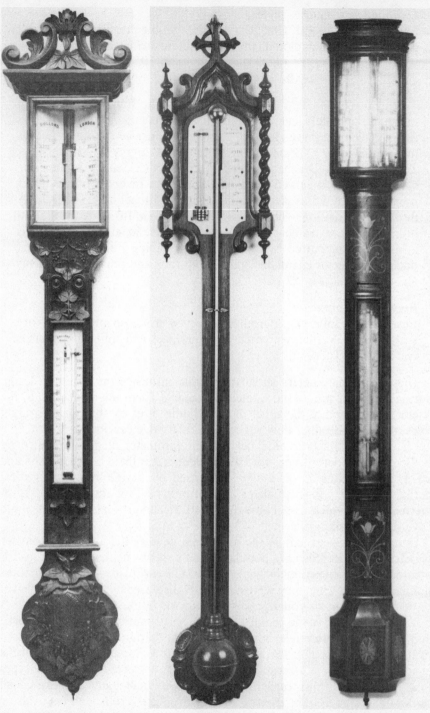

Fig. 184 Carved oak pediment barometer with maximum and minimum thermometer by Dollond, London, c. 1875 (*Christies, London*). Fig. 185 Carved oak cistern barometer by B. Boese, Kidderminster, c. 1875. Fig. 186 Mahogany cistern barometer by Negretti & Zambra, London, c. 1900 (*Christies, London*).

138

The barometer could be described as late Victorian or Edwardian and some would say it is a reproduction, but barometers continued to be made, based on earlier designs, in the twentieth century and until today. These are mainly copies of the portable model barometer of the 1870s and the broken pediment barometer of the 1830s.

7

Angle Tube Barometers

Shortly after it was realised that the extremes of atmospheric pressure only varied the height of the column of mercury by a maximum of 3 inches, many scientists considered ways and means of enlarging the reading by extending the scale. Various instruments were designed with this objective in mind, but it was Sir Samuel Morland (*Fig.* 187) who, before 1680, thought of a simple modification to the straight tube which achieved this result.

He bent a tube sharply to almost a right-angle just below the lowest point to which the mercury could fall and extended the arm to about 36 inches. The arm rose about 3 inches along its length so that for every inch the mercury rose it had to travel 12 inches along the arm, resulting in a scale magnification of twelve to one. The tube was bent between 27 and 28 inches above the level of mercury in the cistern and the scale extended from 28 to 31 inches along the angled tube. This was the basis of the angle tube barometer.

Samuel Morland was the son of Thomas Morland, rector of Sulhamstead Bannister, Berkshire. He became a mathematician and also invented the balance barometer, but only a very few were made as they had a number of disadvantages. His most important work was in the field of hydrostatics, and he invented an apparatus using an airtight cistern from which air was expelled by a charge of gunpowder, the water below rising to fill the vacuum produced. There was great interest in the mid-seventeenth century in mechanical methods of raising water and Morland was the leader in this field. King Charles II, who knighted him, named him 'Master of Mechanics' in 1681. He married five times but was survived by only one son, called Samuel.

The angle barometer was never regarded as a scientific instrument as its accuracy was impaired by the shape of the mercury meniscus, which varied between rising and falling conditions, so offsetting the effect of the magnified scale; the reading was also affected by friction between the mercury and the tube. However, as a domestic barometer it achieved some popularity and was produced, in small numbers, for almost two hundred years. Because of their appearance they are variously called sign post, yard arm, inclined or diagonal barometers.

This type of barometer was not, at first, in much demand because of its shape, and John Smith, when writing about the baroscope or quicksilver weather-glass in 1688, noted that: 'These do manifest the least motions of the

140

Fig. 187 Sir Samuel Morland (1625–96).

mercury more visibly than that with the straight tube', and also that: 'This form was but seldom used being such as will not admit of any regular figure'.

One of the earliest angle barometer-makers was Daniel Quare, and a particularly fine example by him can be seen at Hampton Court. The frame is of turned walnut similar in appearance to the Quare barometer in *Fig.* 23, and the silvered brass register plates are 20 inches in length and cover a 2 inch rise in the mercury from 28½ inches to 30½ inches, a magnification of ten. The barometer was made around 1700.

John Patrick was another early maker who advertised four different types of diagonal barometer in his advertisement of around 1710 (*Fig.* 25). He overcame the main criticism that the barometer lacked balance by mounting it on a square or rectangular frame and incorporating a large looking glass in the central section. To balance the vertical section of the mercury tube at one side of the frame he added a large thermometer at the other side and used identical covers for the cistern and the thermometer bulb. He advertised the instrument as follows:

An excellent diagonal barometer with a looking-glass commodiously placed on the same frame, between the barometer and the thermometer, whereby gentlemen and ladies at the same time they dress may accommodate their habit to the weather – an invention not only curious but also profitable and pleasant.

Patrick sold this type of barometer for fifteen guineas in 1710. The advertisement shows that the cases were of walnut with moulded edges and turned cistern covers. All the barometers appear to have portable screws, although the Royal Society scale thermometers have similar attachments.

The barometer numbered 11 in the advertisement and described as 'A Diagonal Barometer the Quicksilver moving at Bottom 30 inches' appears to have been copied from one invented by Francis Hauksbee and mentioned by John Harris in his *Lexicon Technicum* of 1704 as follows:

The ingenious Mr. Hauksbee shewed me a Baroscope where the mercury rose and fell 60 inches with very great ease, and without breaking or dividing; and it may very easily be made for 100 or 200 inches, if a strait small thin glass tube can be blown and drawn of that length, and that it were as easily manageable.

An engraving of Hauksbee's rather more elaborate barometer was shown; a cistern tube was used with a glass tube fixed in the side of the cistern and extending at a slight angle for 60 inches. This tube was calibrated and recorded the height of the mercury in the cistern.

This type of angle barometer never became popular and only a comparatively few angle instruments of the standard type were made during the eighteenth century, as the stick barometer was by far the most popular and, of course, much cheaper. However, a variety was made by a limited number of makers, the main difference between them being the length of the arm. It

Fig. 188 Mahogany angle barometer with thermometer, hygrometer and mirror signed T. Blunt, London, c. 1725 (*Hotspur Ltd, London*).

143

was, of course, easy to increase the length of the scale by reducing the angle of the tube, and some barometers were made with the horizontal section of the tube twice as long as the vertical.

An angle barometer with a thermometer, hygrometer and mirror is illustrated in *Fig.* 188. The mahogany case is heavily carved with masks and scrolls in the Baroque style and the architectural cornice suggests the William Kent influence (c.1730). The silvered brass register plates have the standard weather indications but the tube and the plates have been slightly shortened, probably in the nineteenth century, to allow for the addition of a Dry/Damp oat-beard hygrometer. The Royal Society scale on the thermometer suggests that the barometer was made not later than the first quarter of the eighteenth century, but the scales are signed T. Blunt, London, who began his apprenticeship to Edward Nairne in 1760. The original thermometer appears to have been replaced and it could be that Blunt undertook this, and the addition of the hygrometer, and engraved his name on the thermometer scales at this time.

In the City Museum and Art Gallery, Birmingham, there is an almost identical barometer signed 'E. Scarlett, London'. He was active between 1712 and 1743 and could well have made both barometers around 1725.

Edward Saul in his 'Account of the Barometer or Weather-Glass' published in 1735 was complimentary about the angle barometer:

> The best and most convenient contrivance for a barometer seems to be that of a sloping tube, rising upright from the stagnant mercury to the height of 28 inches; and then reclining and running off in an angle, to a length of 12 inches, and to a perpendicular height of 3 inches; according to which frame, for every inch that the mercury rises in the perpendicular tube, it will rise 4 inches in the sloping tube; and therby make any changes in the gravitation of the air more discernable.

> Besides these, there are other barometers of a more modern invention, contrived so as to encreate the rise and fall of the mercury to 30, 60 or even to 100 inches; but then as they are more nice and accurate in their construction, and difficult in their management, they are fitter for the closets and speculations of philosophers, than to be introduced into common use, or accommodated to the ordinary capacities of mankind.

Such barometers were unsightly and unwieldy, and a way of reducing the horizontal length without reducing the scale was devised. This was to use two or three separate tubes, set side by side, with each one angled at a slightly different height so that the two or three horizontal tubes would cover the full scale. For example, if there were three tubes and the scale was to extend from 28 inches to 31 inches, the first tube would be angled at 28 inches, the second at 29 inches and the third at 30 inches. Each horizontal section would rise 1 inch along its length so that when the reading was 29½ inches, the lower horizontal tube would be full, with the middle tube half full and the upper tube empty.

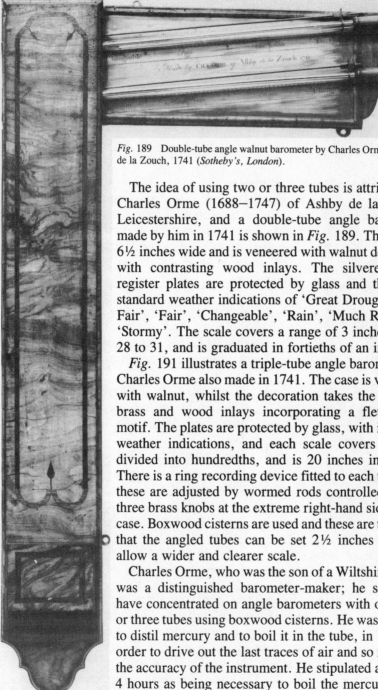

Fig. 189   Double-tube angle walnut barometer by Charles Orme of Ashby de la Zouch, 1741 (*Sotheby's, London*).

The idea of using two or three tubes is attributed to Charles Orme (1688–1747) of Ashby de la Zouch, Leicestershire, and a double-tube angle barometer made by him in 1741 is shown in *Fig.* 189. The case is 6½ inches wide and is veneered with walnut decorated with contrasting wood inlays. The silvered brass register plates are protected by glass and there are standard weather indications of 'Great Drought', 'Set Fair', 'Fair', 'Changeable', 'Rain', 'Much Rain' and 'Stormy'. The scale covers a range of 3 inches, from 28 to 31, and is graduated in fortieths of an inch.

Fig. 191 illustrates a triple-tube angle barometer by Charles Orme also made in 1741. The case is veneered with walnut, whilst the decoration takes the form of brass and wood inlays incorporating a fleur-de-lis motif. The plates are protected by glass, with identical weather indications, and each scale covers 1 inch, divided into hundredths, and is 20 inches in length. There is a ring recording device fitted to each tube and these are adjusted by wormed rods controlled by the three brass knobs at the extreme right-hand side of the case. Boxwood cisterns are used and these are tiered so that the angled tubes can be set 2½ inches apart to allow a wider and clearer scale.

Charles Orme, who was the son of a Wiltshire vicar, was a distinguished barometer-maker; he seems to have concentrated on angle barometers with one, two or three tubes using boxwood cisterns. He was the first to distil mercury and to boil it in the tube, in 1738, in order to drive out the last traces of air and so improve the accuracy of the instrument. He stipulated a time of 4 hours as being necessary to boil the mercury in an angle tube 49 inches long.

Very interesting and sought after angle barometers are those with a 'Perpetual Regulation of Time', as

145

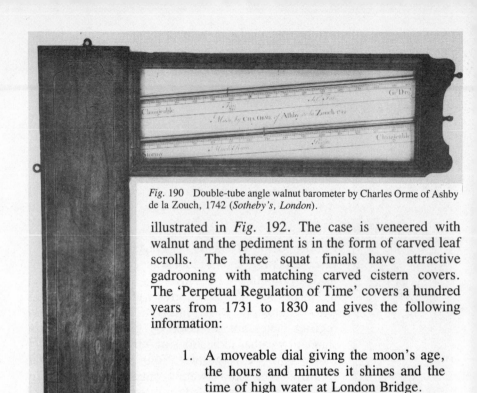

Fig. 190   Double-tube angle walnut barometer by Charles Orme of Ashby de la Zouch, 1742 (*Sotheby's, London*).

illustrated in *Fig.* 192. The case is veneered with walnut and the pediment is in the form of carved leaf scrolls. The three squat finials have attractive gadrooning with matching carved cistern covers. The 'Perpetual Regulation of Time' covers a hundred years from 1731 to 1830 and gives the following information:

1. A moveable dial giving the moon's age, the hours and minutes it shines and the time of high water at London Bridge.
2. A moveable dial giving the days of the month.
3. A moveable dial giving the Zodiac signs, the fixed feasts, sun rise and sun set, day break and day length, and equation of days.
4. Epochs and Dominical letters for 1731 to 1830.
5. Easter days from 1731 to 1830 to calculate the moveable feasts.
6. A Regal table from William I 1066 to George II 1727.
7. A chart of moveable feasts.
8. Two sections of Explanation.

The three movable dials are operated by three wooden knobs at the back of the case.

The spirit thermometer has a Fahrenheit scale and the painted paper almanac is protected by glass. The barometer is unsigned but was probably made shortly before 1731, the year the almanac commenced.

A similar barometer, made at least twenty years later by John Cuff, is shown in *Fig.* 193. The case is veneered with mahogany with an adjustable oat-beard

146

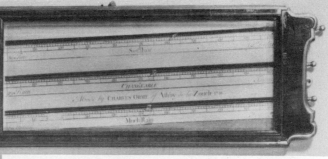

Fig. 191 Triple-tube angle walnut barometer by Charles Orme of Ashby de la Zouch, 1741 (*Hotspur Ltd, London*).

hygrometer mounted between a broken pediment, the top of which is decorated with fretwork. A portable tube is used and the thermometer has a Fahrenheit scale.

The 'Perpetual Regulation of Time', which is printed on paper and protected by glass, differs from the one just described in two respects: it covers the years 1753–1852, and the five scenes are all slightly different. There are four key holes on the case; the one between the hygrometer and the register plates operates the hygrometer; the one above the almanac operates the movable dial giving the high-water times at London Bridge; the one on the right of the almanac controls the movable dial giving the days of the month and the one on the left of the almanac operates the movable dial giving the signs of the Zodiac. They all operate by large interacting cogs.

The name of Francis Watkins is associated with this type of angle barometer; examples are extant signed by him, but far more appear to have been made during a partnership between him and one of his former apprentices, Addison Smith. The partnership was operated from 5 Charing Cross, London, but as it only lasted for eleven years between 1763 and 1774 their instruments can be dated fairly accurately.

The angle barometers illustrated in *Figs.* 194 and 195 are both signed Watkins & Smith, London, and can be dated c. 1765 and c. 1770, respectively. Both are veneered with mahogany and have gadrooning on the cistern covers. The almanacs are identical to the one used by J. Cuff (*Fig.* 193) and cover the years 1753 to 1852. The

147

Fig. 192   Walnut angle barometer with a 'Perpetual Regulation of Time'. Unsigned, c. 1735 (*Hotspur Ltd, London*).

148

Fig. 193   Mahogany angle barometer with a 'Perpetual Regulation of Time' by J. Cuff, c. 1755 (*Hotspur Ltd, London*).

149

Fig. 194 Mahogany angle barometer with a 'Perpetual Regulation of Time' by Watkins & Smith, c. 1765 (British Crown Copyright, *Science Museum, London*).

Fig. 195 Mahogany angle barometer with a 'Perpetual Regulation of Time' by Watkins & Smith, London, c. 1770 (*Hotspur Ltd, London*).

differences are that the barometer in *Fig.* 194 has a triangular pediment and three finials whilst the barometer in *Fig.* 195 has no pediment but the case is bordered by decorative stringing. The original thermometer appears to have been replaced and the fact that it has a groove for the pointer rather than a wire, suggests that it was made a little later. Both barometer scales have a magnification of six.

An angle barometer with a 'Perpetual Regulation of Time' covering the years 1773 to 1872 is illustrated in *Fig.* 196. All five scenes again differ in detail from the two earlier prints of the almanac and in this case 'George III 1760' is added to 'The Regal Table'. The case is lined of mahogany and there is a straight tube barometer with a vernier in addition to the angle tube. The style of the case and the almanac suggests that it was made around 1775 but the register plates are engraved 'Negretti & Zambra, London'. This partnership was not formed until 1850 so it must be an excellent reproduction if they made it. The hygrometer is certainly nineteenth century, and a possible explanation could be that Negretti & Zambra restored it and signed it at that time.

The early angle barometers were veneered in walnut but mahogany was preferred from around the middle of the eighteenth century. A few were lacquered with japan to make them black and glossy and some were decorated with marquetry: a later decoration was the use of inlays, including the shell motif, on cistern covers, which became so popular on the wheel type of barometer.

Because of its unattractive shape and the difficulty of decorating it, the angle barometer never achieved the popularity of the stick and wheel varieties. Because of the limited demand there were comparatively few makers, and the barometers they produced were generally of their own distinctive design. A second attempt was made, around 1750, to improve the shape by reintroducing a wall mirror and an example is shown in *Fig.* 197.

The case is veneered with mahogany and the broken architectural pediment is centred with a brass finial in the shape of an urn. The barometer and thermometer both have silvered brass register plates and both are fitted with a sliding indicating pointer. Spirally turned cistern covers protect both instruments and a Fair/Rain hygrometer is fitted centrally below the register plates. A spirit level is incorporated in the shaped apron, and the overall height is 3 feet 4 inches. The barometer is unsigned but can be dated c. 1760.

A barometer with a particularly long arm is shown in *Fig.* 198. The mahogany case has a turned hemispherical cistern cover and an engraved circular brass cover at the angle; this extends to 39 inches giving a magnification of ten times. The silvered brass register plates are engraved J. Linnell, Ludgate Street, London; he was apprenticed to James Ayscough in 1754 and succeeded him in 1763. On his trade card he described himself as an optician but he sold all sorts of instruments including barometers, diagonal, standard and portable.

An interesting angle barometer made by John Finney of Liverpool around 1770 is illustrated in *Fig.* 199. The straight-lined architectural mahogany case has a fluted trunk and a dentil moulding under the cornice which is

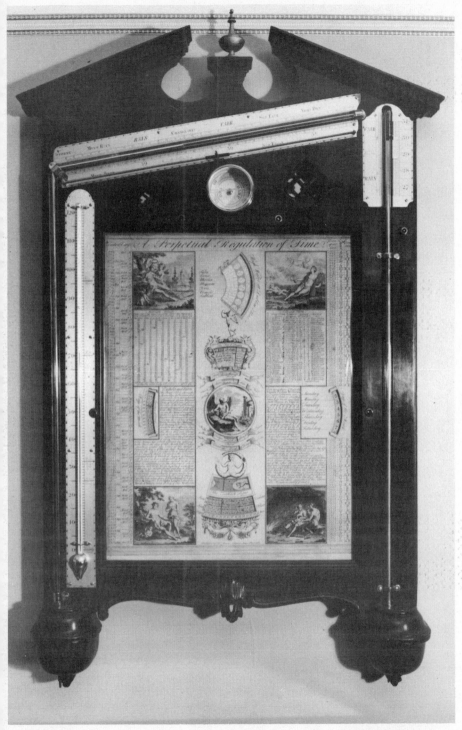

Fig. 196   Mahogany angle barometer with a 'Perpetual Regulation of Time' signed Negretti & Zambra, c. 1775 (*G. E. Marsh, Winchester*).

Fig. 197 Mahogany angle tube barometer with mirror. Unsigned, c. 1760 (*Sotheby's, London*).

Fig. 198 Mahogany angle barometer by J. Linnell, Ludgate Street, London, c. 1765 (*Christies, London*). *Fig.* 199 Mahogany angle barometer by Finney, Liverpool, c. 1770 (*Science Museum, London*).

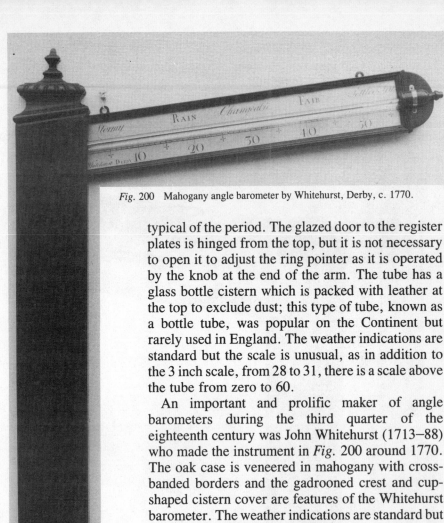

Fig. 200   Mahogany angle barometer by Whitehurst, Derby, c. 1770.

typical of the period. The glazed door to the register plates is hinged from the top, but it is not necessary to open it to adjust the ring pointer as it is operated by the knob at the end of the arm. The tube has a glass bottle cistern which is packed with leather at the top to exclude dust; this type of tube, known as a bottle tube, was popular on the Continent but rarely used in England. The weather indications are standard but the scale is unusual, as in addition to the 3 inch scale, from 28 to 31, there is a scale above the tube from zero to 60.

An important and prolific maker of angle barometers during the third quarter of the eighteenth century was John Whitehurst (1713–88) who made the instrument in *Fig.* 200 around 1770. The oak case is veneered in mahogany with cross-banded borders and the gadrooned crest and cup-shaped cistern cover are features of the Whitehurst barometer. The weather indications are standard but the scale, like the Finney barometer, is from 0 to 60. The silvered brass register plates are protected by glass which is fixed flush to the plates; they extend to 21 inches giving a magnification of seven. The tube and the solid-base boxwood cistern appear to be as originally fitted.

John Whitehurst was a clockmaker, instrument-maker and assayer. He started in business as a clockmaker in Derby in 1736 and became well known for his turret clocks; he also invented the 'tell-tale' clock. In 1775, he moved to London to become 'Stamper of Money Weights' at the Mint but still continued to make clocks, and his house was said to be 'the common resort of the scientific and ingenious of all ranks and nations'. His book 'An Enquiry into the Original State and Formation

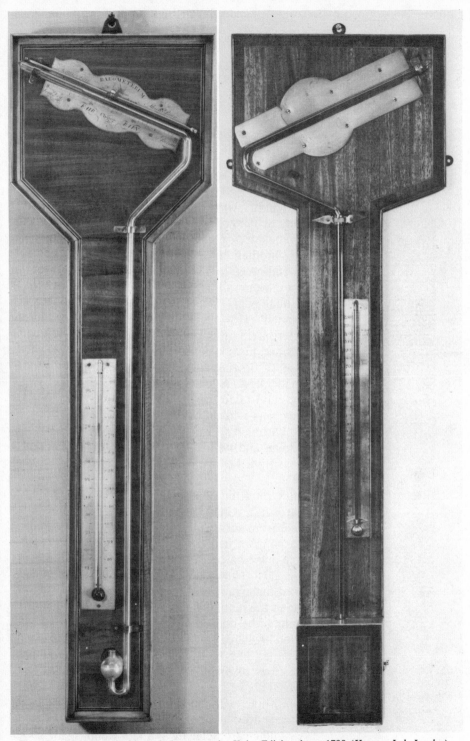

Fig. 201 Mahogany double-angle barometer by Knie, Edinburgh, c. 1790 (*Hotspur Ltd, London*).
Fig. 202 Mahogany double-angle barometer by William Robb, Montrose, c. 1800.

157

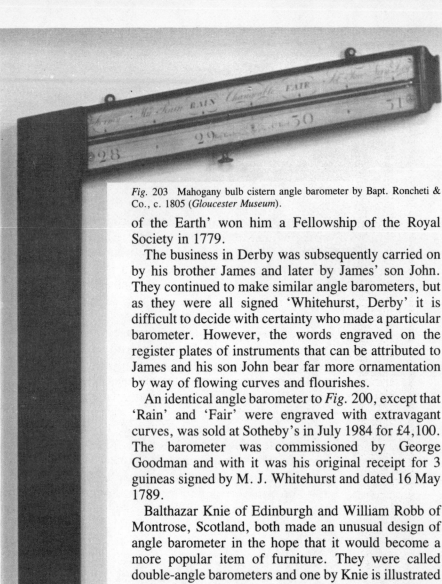

Fig. 203 Mahogany bulb cistern angle barometer by Bapt. Roncheti & Co., c. 1805 (*Gloucester Museum*).

of the Earth' won him a Fellowship of the Royal Society in 1779.

The business in Derby was subsequently carried on by his brother James and later by James' son John. They continued to make similar angle barometers, but as they were all signed 'Whitehurst, Derby' it is difficult to decide with certainty who made a particular barometer. However, the words engraved on the register plates of instruments that can be attributed to James and his son John bear far more ornamentation by way of flowing curves and flourishes.

An identical angle barometer to *Fig.* 200, except that 'Rain' and 'Fair' were engraved with extravagant curves, was sold at Sotheby's in July 1984 for £4,100. The barometer was commissioned by George Goodman and with it was his original receipt for 3 guineas signed by M. J. Whitehurst and dated 16 May 1789.

Balthazar Knie of Edinburgh and William Robb of Montrose, Scotland, both made an unusual design of angle barometer in the hope that it would become a more popular item of furniture. They were called double-angle barometers and one by Knie is illustrated in *Fig.* 201. The case is veneered with an attractively grained mahogany with boxwood stringing round the inside of the moulded edges. The double angle allows the tube to be housed on a symmetrical base with the silvered brass register plates extending to the width of the frame. The scale is from 28 to 31 inches with graduations of one-tenth of an inch. 'Knie, Edin.' is engraved above the plates which are decorated with a six-point star, with the word 'Barometerum' above. It was made around 1790.

A similar barometer by William Robb, made about ten years later, is shown in *Fig.* 202. The case is

158

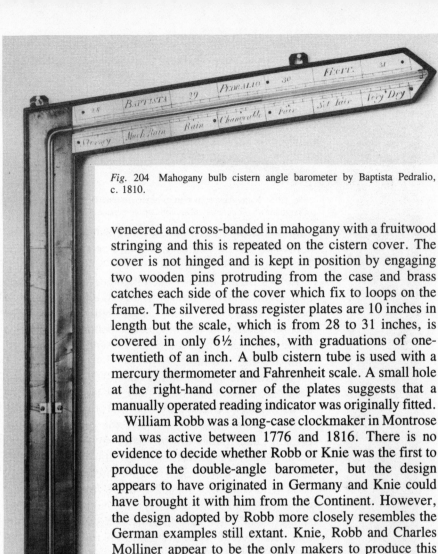

Fig. 204 Mahogany bulb cistern angle barometer by Baptista Pedralio, c. 1810.

veneered and cross-banded in mahogany with a fruitwood stringing and this is repeated on the cistern cover. The cover is not hinged and is kept in position by engaging two wooden pins protruding from the case and brass catches each side of the cover which fix to loops on the frame. The silvered brass register plates are 10 inches in length but the scale, which is from 28 to 31 inches, is covered in only 6½ inches, with graduations of one-twentieth of an inch. A bulb cistern tube is used with a mercury thermometer and Fahrenheit scale. A small hole at the right-hand corner of the plates suggests that a manually operated reading indicator was originally fitted.

William Robb was a long-case clockmaker in Montrose and was active between 1776 and 1816. There is no evidence to decide whether Robb or Knie was the first to produce the double-angle barometer, but the design appears to have originated in Germany and Knie could have brought it with him from the Continent. However, the design adopted by Robb more closely resembles the German examples still extant. Knie, Robb and Charles Molliner appear to be the only makers to produce this type of barometer commercially in the United Kingdom, so it must be said that they failed in their attempt to popularise the angle barometer.

A limited number of makers, including Italian immigrants, continued to make angle barometers in the nineteenth century; the cases were usually of mahogany with bulb cistern tubes but there were exceptions.

Baptis Roncheti, a prolific maker of stick, wheel and multiple-tube barometers, also made angle barometers including the one in *Fig.* 203 early in the nineteenth century. The case is veneered in mahogany with a shallow turned cistern cover which contains a bulb cistern. The silvered register plates are 18 inches long and the scale is divided into tenths of an inch. The sliding

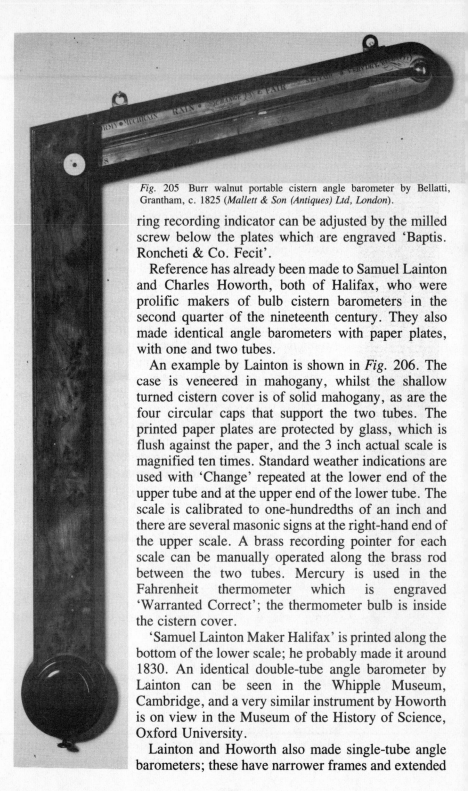

Fig. 205 Burr walnut portable cistern angle barometer by Bellatti, Grantham, c. 1825 (*Mallett & Son (Antiques) Ltd, London*).

ring recording indicator can be adjusted by the milled screw below the plates which are engraved 'Baptis. Roncheti & Co. Fecit'.

Reference has already been made to Samuel Lainton and Charles Howorth, both of Halifax, who were prolific makers of bulb cistern barometers in the second quarter of the nineteenth century. They also made identical angle barometers with paper plates, with one and two tubes.

An example by Lainton is shown in *Fig.* 206. The case is veneered in mahogany, whilst the shallow turned cistern cover is of solid mahogany, as are the four circular caps that support the two tubes. The printed paper plates are protected by glass, which is flush against the paper, and the 3 inch actual scale is magnified ten times. Standard weather indications are used with 'Change' repeated at the lower end of the upper tube and at the upper end of the lower tube. The scale is calibrated to one-hundredths of an inch and there are several masonic signs at the right-hand end of the upper scale. A brass recording pointer for each scale can be manually operated along the brass rod between the two tubes. Mercury is used in the Fahrenheit thermometer which is engraved 'Warranted Correct'; the thermometer bulb is inside the cistern cover.

'Samuel Lainton Maker Halifax' is printed along the bottom of the lower scale; he probably made it around 1830. An identical double-tube angle barometer by Lainton can be seen in the Whipple Museum, Cambridge, and a very similar instrument by Howorth is on view in the Museum of the History of Science, Oxford University.

Lainton and Howorth also made single-tube angle barometers; these have narrower frames and extended

160

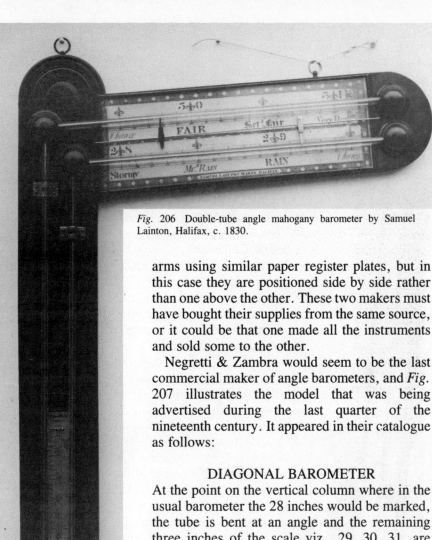

Fig. 206 Double-tube angle mahogany barometer by Samuel
Lainton, Halifax, c. 1830.

arms using similar paper register plates, but in
this case they are positioned side by side rather
than one above the other. These two makers must
have bought their supplies from the same source,
or it could be that one made all the instruments
and sold some to the other.

Negretti & Zambra would seem to be the last
commercial maker of angle barometers, and *Fig.*
207 illustrates the model that was being
advertised during the last quarter of the
nineteenth century. It appeared in their catalogue
as follows:

DIAGONAL BAROMETER

At the point on the vertical column where in the
usual barometer the 28 inches would be marked,
the tube is bent at an angle and the remaining
three inches of the scale viz., 29, 30, 31, are
extended over a tube 36 inches long. The
mercury moving diagonally travels over 12
inches of the tube for every inch on the vertical
scale, adding to the interest of the instrument, as
the slightest variations are thereby magnified,
and are at once very noticeable, whereas they
would be overlooked on the ordinary barometer.

The tube is mounted on a stout well-made
frame of oak or mahogany with engraved
silvered metal scales, and with two setting
indices. The instrument has a flexible cistern,
and can be made portable for transit.

Price £10 0 0

161

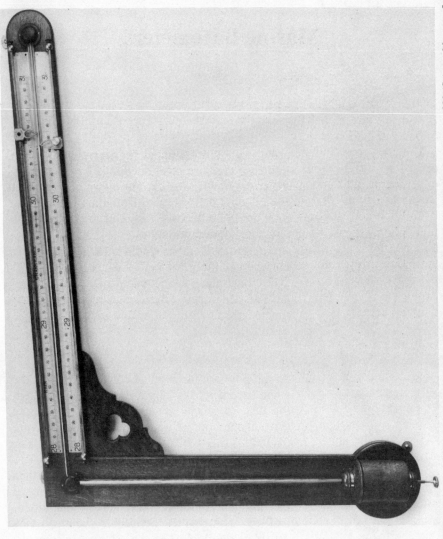

Fig. 207 Oak angle barometer by Negretti & Zambra, Scientific Instrument Makers, London, c. 1880 (*Science Museum, London*).

8

Marine Barometers

There is some doubt as to when the first barometer was used at sea, but there is evidence that in 1667 the scientist Robert Hooke appreciated the advantage of being able to measure the air pressure whilst at sea.

The main problem was to prevent the oscillation of the mercury in the tube caused by the motions of the ship and Hooke conducted a number of experiments in an endeavour to overcome this. He presented a paper to the Royal Society in 1668 in which he suggested two methods.

The first consisted of an air thermometer, with mercury as an indicating liquid, and a spirit thermometer to record the temperature. The variations in air pressure were recorded by the rise or fall of the mercury in the air thermometer with adjustments being made for temperature after reference to the spirit thermometer. Such an instrument was taken on a voyage of exploration in the Atlantic in 1698 by Edmond Halley, a notable astronomer, who reported:

It never failed to prognostick and give early notice of all the bad weather we had, so that I depended thereon, and made provision accordingly; and from my own experience I conclude that a more useful contrivance hath not for this long time been offered for the benefit of navigation.

This was the same type of instrument as advertised by John Patrick in his advertisement of c. 1710 (see *Fig.* 25). It is numbered 2 and described as 'A Ship Barometer' 'A Foot Long'. It was in use for many years and should, perhaps, be described as a thermobarometer.

The second method suggested by Hooke was to constrict the tube to a fine bore at the lower end, just above the cistern, and this had the effect of containing the oscillations to an acceptable level.

Nothing further seems to have happened to this invention until 1773 – more than a hundred years later – when an improved form of constricted-tube barometer was taken on a scientific voyage, towards the North Pole, undertaken by His Majesty's Command. The officer in charge, Captain C. J. Phipps, Second Baron Mulgrave, published an account of the voyage and described the instruments aboard, which included a marine barometer made by Edward Nairne:

The bore of the upper part of the glass tube of this barometer is about three-tenths of an inch in diameter, and four inches long. To this is joined a glass tube with a bore about one-twentieth of an inch in diameter. The two glass tubes being joined together form the tube of the barometer.

In a common barometer the motion of the mercury up and down in the tube is so great that it is not possible to measure its perpendicular height; consequently, cannot shew any alteration in the weight of the atmosphere, but in this marine barometer that defect is remedied. The instrument is fixed in gimmals and kept in a perpendicular position by a weight fastened to the bottom of it.

This type of construction proved to be successful at sea and was used, with improvements, for upwards of a hundred years.

Edward Nairne (1726–1806) has already been mentioned as the partner of Thomas Blunt. He was an optical, mathematical and philosophical instrument-maker and published literature on astronomical and navigational instruments. He made diagonal, portable and marine barometers at his workshop at 20 Cornhill, London. The demand for marine barometers, however, was very limited and they were not made in any quantity until the beginning of the nineteenth century.

An early marine barometer made around 1805 by Berge, London, is illustrated in *Fig.* 208. It is housed in a round mahogany case with brass top, gimbals and cistern cover. The silvered brass register plates have a scale from 28 to 31 inches with divisions of one-tenth of an inch and a vernier which is operated by the milled screw on the right of the scales. The plates are only engraved with the maker's name and 'Change', above which is 'Fair if Mercury Rise' and below 'Foul if Mercury Fall'. The thermometer has Fahrenheit and centigrade scales.

Fig. 209 shows a marine barometer made

Fig. 208 Mahogany marine barometer by Berge, London, late Ramsden, c. 1805 (*The National Maritime Museum, London*).

164

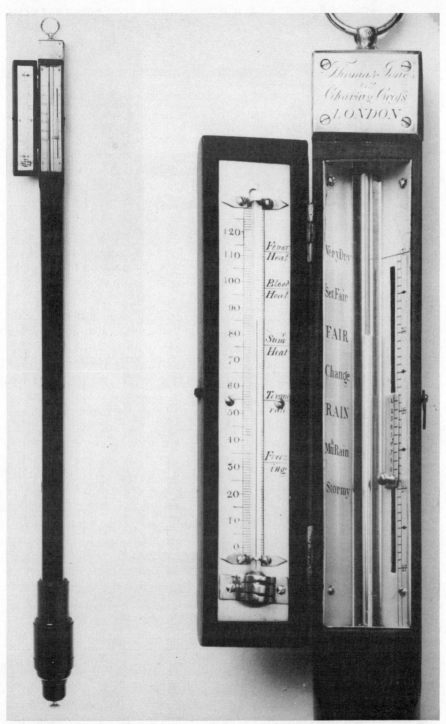

Fig. 209 Mahogany marine barometer by Thomas Jones, 62 Charing Cross, London, c. 1820 (*Patric Capon, London*).

Fig. 210 Mahogany marine barometer with gimbals by T. Bennett, Cork, c. 1820 (*Patric Capon, London*).

by Thomas Jones of 62 Charing Cross, London, c. 1820. The top 8 inches of the tube have a bore of approximately three-tenths of an inch whilst the remainder of the tube has a bore with a diameter little more than that of a pin. The tube is cemented to the cistern, which is of boxwood and has a leather base and portable screw. The solid mahogany case has a hinged door to be opened when a reading is to be taken. The silvered brass register plates are set aslant to give them an increased width, and a manual vernier is fitted. The boxwood cistern is ebonised on the outside and can be unscrewed from the case.

The barometer can be hung on a wall or mounted on a gimbals, for which there is a hole on each side of the case 6 inches below the door. The weight of the cistern, together with the weight of the mercury it contains, is sufficient to ensure that the barometer moves on the bearings and always remains in an upright position.

This type of marine barometer, with a thermometer on the door, remained popular until around 1865, with one or two alterations. Around 1830 brass silvered register plates began to be replaced by ivory plates and the boxwood cistern was reduced in size and given a brass cover.

Fig. 211 illustrates a mahogany cased marine barometer with ivory register plates and ivory thermometer scales. There are the seven standard weather indications, as shown in *Fig.* 209, but the thermometer has Fahrenheit and Réaumur scales. The portable boxwood cistern is contained in a brass cover which is screwed to the case. The maker's name, Dring & Fage, 20 Tooley Street, London, is engraved on an ivory plate above the door. This was an important firm of barometer- and thermometer-makers between 1798 and 1860, which operated from 20 Tooley Street between 1822 and 1845.

The cistern cover was slightly altered in the 1830s in that the portable screw was incorporated within the cistern cover. The shape of the cover was then as shown in *Fig.* 212. It is made of brass for protection and the bottom rim portion unscrews to give access to the portable screw beneath the cistern. Although there is no glass to protect the register plates, there is an aperture below the plates for a key to adjust the vernier. The ivory plate is engraved Spencer Browning & Co., London, who were optical and mathematical instrument-makers between 1783 and 1838.

By about 1840 the round-top marine barometer was introduced, as illustrated in *Fig.* 214. The ivory register plates are protected by glass, which is fixed, and a vernier with rackwork is necessary. The thermometer is contained in a separate box on the panelled trunk; it too has ivory Fahrenheit scales. Jones of Dublin is the maker.

This type of barometer was offered in mahogany, rosewood or oak cases and, if the case was made of rosewood, it could be decorated with mother-of-pearl as in *Fig.* 215. The barometer was made around 1840 by Spencer Browning & Co., Minories, London. Its height is 37 inches.

Marine barometers were also sold in very attractively carved cases as in *Figs.* 217–19. They were usually in mahogany and were often purchased to decorate private houses rather than for use on board ship.

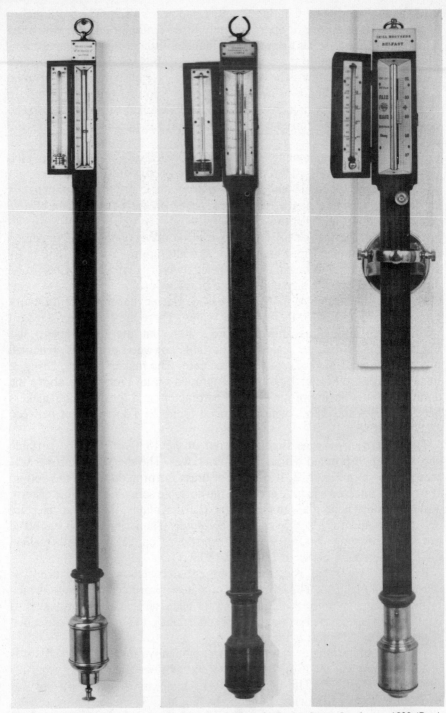

Fig. 211 Mahogany marine barometer by Dring & Fage, 20 Tooley Street, London, c. 1830 (*Patric Capon, London*). *Fig.* 212 Mahogany marine barometer by Spencer Browning & Co., London, c. 1835 (*M. W. Cox, Bristol*). *Fig.* 213 Mahogany marine barometer with ivory register plates by Neill Brothers, Belfast, c. 1835 (*Park Street Antiques, Berkhamstead*).

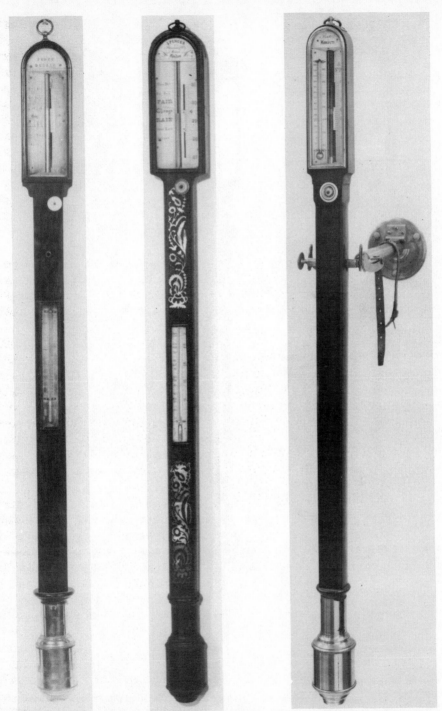

Fig. 214 Mahogany marine barometer by Jones, Dublin, c. 1840. *Fig.* 215 Rosewood marine barometer by Spencer Browning & Co., Minories, London, c. 1840. *Fig.* 216 Mahogany marine barometer with brass glazed plate cover and gimbals by Bate, London, c. 1840 (*Science Museum, London*).

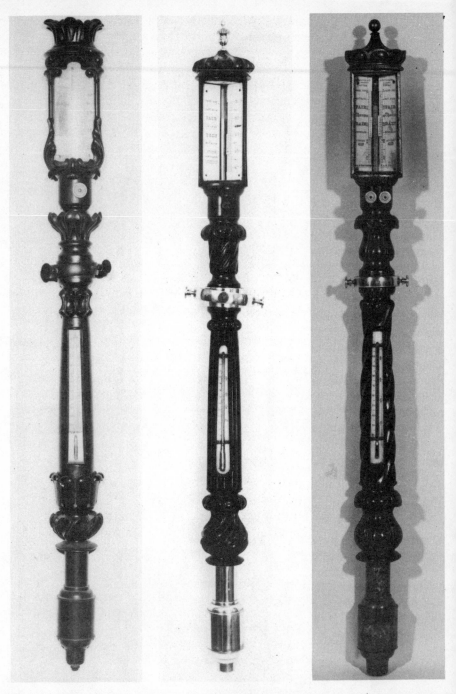

Fig. 217 Mahogany marine barometer in cylindrical tapering case carved with foliate scrolls and crown. Ivory register plates. 38 inches overall. Unsigned, c. 1840 (*Christies, London*). *Fig.* 218 Mahogany marine barometer in cylindrical tapering case decorated with fluting, reeding and gadrooning. Ivory register plates by I. & A. Walker, Liverpool, c. 1840 (*Park Street Antiques, Berkhamstead*). *Fig.* 219 Mahogany marine barometer in decorated cylindrical tapering case with painted brass cistern cover by Melling & Co., Opticians, Liverpool, c. 1840 (*Mallett & Son (Antiques) Ltd, London*).

170

Although marine barometers with wooden cases continued to be made into the last quarter of the nineteenth century, a new improved design was developed around 1855 by John Welsh of the Kew Observatory and Patrick Adie, a London instrument-maker. It was the outcome of an international conference called in Brussels in 1853 for the purpose of devising a systematic plan for promoting meteorological observations at sea. Various recommendations were made by the Brussels Conference and these were adopted by the British Government, which encouraged the Kew Committee of the British Association to develop a marine barometer, incorporating the recommendations.

Welsh and Adie worked together at Kew Observatory and produced a marine barometer identical to the one shown in *Fig.* 220 and made by Adie in 1857. The glass tube is protected by a brass tubular frame into which is screwed an iron cistern which is completely closed except for a small aperture open to the atmosphere. The tube has the usual constricted bore and in addition has a Bunten air trap below the constriction. This consisted of an elongated funnel, with the point downwards, set in the centre of the tube, rather like a pipette, which prevented any air working its way up between the glass and the mercury to reach the vacuum. Bunten of Paris invented the air trap in 1824.

A Fahrenheit thermometer is fixed to the frame, with the bulb enclosed within the frame so that it accurately records the temperature of the mercury in the tube. A brass ring, movable in a collar fixed on the frame above the centre of gravity of the barometer, is attached to gimbals and supported by a brass arm. A sheath of glass protects the silvered brass register plates, and a vernier allows readings to five-hundredths of an inch. The scale is from 26 to 32 inches but no weather indications are used as these were deemed to be misleading.

The register plates are engraved 'Adie, London' with a crown and 'B.T. No.171'. It was issued to the Board of Trade in February 1858 and was used in various ships until November 1889; it passed to the Science Museum in 1892. There was very little change in the form of the barometer, which was called the Kew pattern marine barometer, from 1855 for a hundred years except that steel replaced the iron cistern and a Gold Slide replaced the thermometer. They were used on land stations as well as at sea.

The maker, Patrick Adie, was a son of Alexander Adie; he was an instrument-maker who specialised in marine barometers from premises at 395 Strand, London, from 1850 to 1884, when he moved to 1 Broadway, Westminster, London. The business continued until 1942.

Although this type of barometer was accepted by the Board of Trade and became the standard issue by the Board to the British Marine, some commercial users, and the French, still gave preference to the wooden frame barometer, as they thought it could be more securely mounted in wood, was more portable and less likely to be broken by a sudden concussion than if fitted in a metal frame. *Figs.* 221–3 illustrate marine barometers in mahogany cases made around 1860.

The name of Admiral Robert Fitzroy is associated with marine

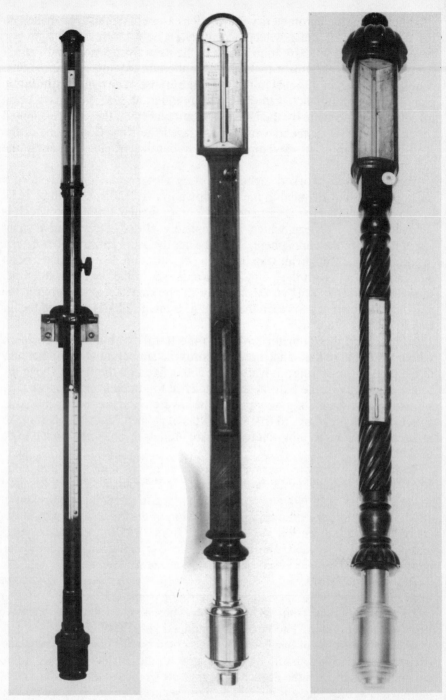

Fig. 220 Kew pattern marine barometer in brass cylindrical case by Adie, London, c. 1857 (British Crown Copyright, *Science Museum, London*).   *Fig.* 221 Mahogany marine barometer with ivory register plates protected by glass and brass cistern cover by J. Sewill, Liverpool, c. 1860.   *Fig.* 222 Mahogany marine barometer with reeding and gadrooning decoration. Ivory register plates, Fahrenheit and Réaumur thermometer scales, by R. Silo, London Bridge, c. 1860.

barometers. Born at Ampton Hall, Suffolk in 1805, he entered the Navy as a cadet just before his thirteenth birthday; later, as Captain of HMS *Beagle,* he undertook survey work with Charles Darwin (1809–82). Fitzroy was elected Member of Parliament for Durham in 1841 and appointed Governor of New Zealand in 1843. On retirement from active service in 1850 he turned his attentions to the science of meteorology and in 1854 was appointed chief of the newly formed Meteorological Department of the Board of Trade.

He considered that the Kew pattern marine barometer was not practical for general use because it was too delicate in construction, difficult to read and was likely to be broken by the firing of a ship's guns. He therefore set out to design a barometer which would overcome these faults and issued the following description:

This marine barometer, for Her Majesty's service, is adapted to general purposes. It differs from barometers hitherto made in points of detail, rather than principle:

1. The glass tube is packed with vulcanised india rubber, which checks vibration from concussion; but does not hold it rigidly, or prevent expansion.

2. It does not oscillate (or pump), though extremely sensitive.

3. The scale is porcelain, very legible, and not liable to change.

4. There is no iron anywhere (to rust).

5. Every part can be unscrewed, examined, or cleaned, by any careful person.

6. There is a spare tube, fixed in a cistern, filled with boiled mercury, and marked for adjustment in this, or any similar instrument.

The barometer is graduated in hundredths, and will be found accurate to that degree, namely the second decimal of an inch. It is packed with vulcanised caoutchouc, in order that (by this, and by a peculiar strength of glass tube) guns may be fired near the instrument without causing injury to it by ordinary concussion. It is hoped that all such instruments, for the public service at sea, will be quite similar, so that any spare tube will fit any barometer.

Negretti & Zambra appear to have been involved in the development of this barometer, and an illustration is given in *Fig.* 224 which is taken from their *Treatise on Meteorological Instruments* dated 1864. The tube is fixed to a boxwood cistern, 'which is plugged with very porous cane at the top, to allow the ready influence of a variation in atmospheric pressure on the mercury'. The frame and all the fittings are of brass. The graduation of inches and decimals are engraved on the right-hand side of the porcelain register plate, with a vernier, and on the left-hand side plate is engraved, 'as legibly as they are expressed succinctly', the following words of interpretation of the barometer movements suggested by Fitzroy:

173

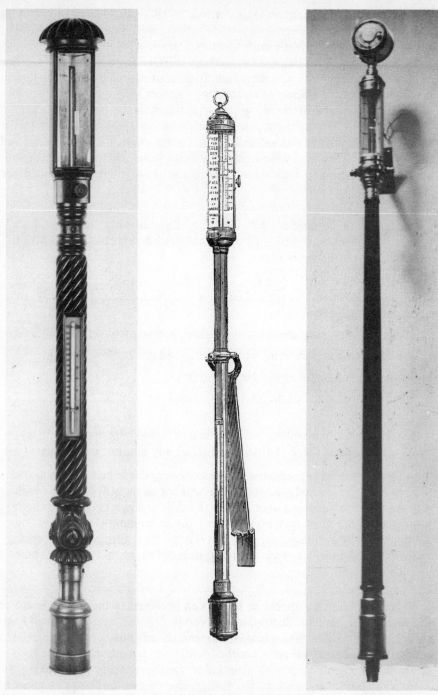

Fig. 223   Mahogany marine barometer in cylindrical case decorated with spiral reeding and gadrooning. Ivory register plates signed C. A. Canti, 30 High Holborn, London, c. 1860.   *Fig.* 224   Fitzroy marine or gun marine barometer by Negretti & Zambra, London, 1864.   *Fig.* 225   Mahogany marine barometer in cylindrical tapering case with brass fittings and circular thermometer above glazed register plates. Unsigned, c. 1870 (*H. W. Keil Ltd, Broadway*).

174

RISE	FALL
for	for
COLD	WARM
DRY	WET
or	or
LESS	MORE
WIND	WIND

A Fahrenheit thermometer is attached to the lower section of the case with the bulb enclosed within the frame next to the tube.

This instrument was called the Fitzroy marine or gun marine barometer and was sold by a number of makers from 1860. There is a very interesting description in the Negretti & Zambra treatise of trials on the Fitzroy marine barometer under fire of guns, some of which Mr Negretti attended. The purpose of the trials was to ascertain whether the vulcanised india rubber packing round the glass tube of the new barometer did check the vibration caused by firing. In a series of experiments a new Fitzroy barometer was tested side by side with a Kew type barometer on HMS *Excellent*. They were hung over the gun, under the gun, by the side of the gun and both inside and outside the bulkhead. The result was that the Kew type barometer was broken and rendered useless, whilst the Fitzroy barometer was not damaged. Five Fitzroy barometers were then subjected to the concussion produced by firing a 68-pounder gun with shot, and 16 lb charge of powder. They were suspended under the gun, then over the gun and finally by a gimbals to a bulkhead at a distance of only 3 feet 6 inches from the axis of the gun. The official report stated that all these barometers, however suspended, would stand, without the slightest injury, the most severe concussion that they would ever be likely to experience in any sea-going man-of-war.

These barometers, like the Kew marine, continued to be made until they were eventually replaced by the aneroid barometer in the twentieth century.

It was evident that these types of barometers were more reliable in their performance than those with wooden frames. The metal frame allowed the tube to be held more rigidly and the graduations could be more accurately made with only temperature having an effect on the readings. The Admiralty favoured the metal-cased barometer, but in spite of this the wooden case was still preferred by some, mainly for its handsome appearance.

Fig. 226 shows a typical mahogany marine barometer made around 1870. It is very similar to the earlier marine barometer except that the weather indications have been reduced to 'Fair', 'Change', 'Rain' and 'Stormy'. The maker was J. Hicks, London, and it was probably made for the European market as it has a Réaumur scale thermometer with C. Mulle Danzig engraved below the bulb; he could have been the retailer.

Carved cases became a feature of this period, and *Figs.* 228 and 229 show a pleasing instrument in solid mahogany with a bow-fronted case, square moulded pediment and foliate carving above the brass cistern cover. The ivory register plates are set aslant and protected by bow glass; they have duplicate weather indications and two verniers so that comparative readings

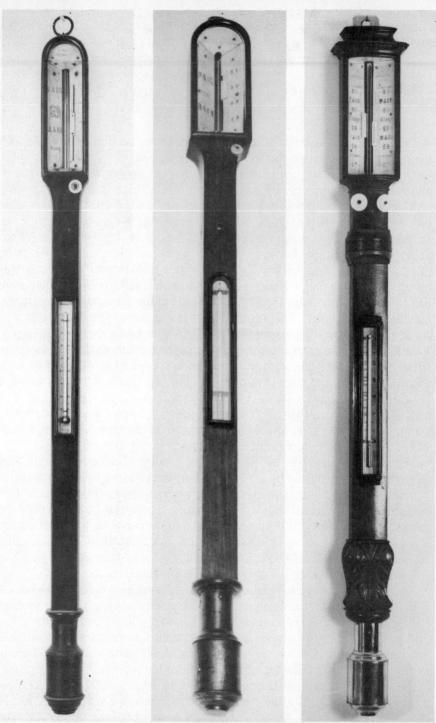

Fig. 226   Mahogany marine barometer with ivory scales by J. Hicks, London, c. 1870.   *Fig.* 227
Mahogany marine barometer with ivory scales. Unsigned, c. 1870.   *Fig.* 228   Mahogany marine
barometer by C. G. Brander & Son, 82 Minories, London, c. 1870.

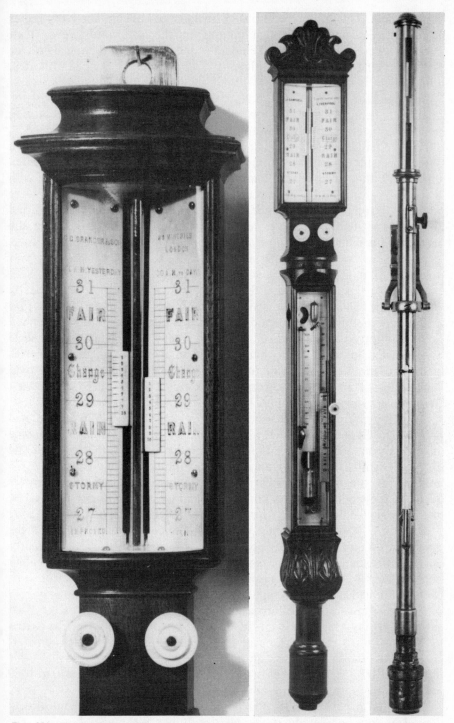

Fig. 229 Detail of *Fig.* 228.   *Fig.* 230 Walnut marine barometer with sympiesometer by
J. Campbell, 7 South Castle Street, Liverpool, c. 1870.   *Fig.* 231 Kew pattern marine barometer in
brass cylindrical case by P. Adie, 1 Broadway, Westminster, c. 1885.

177

can be taken. The thermometer has its own glazed case and the ivory scales have Fahrenheit and Réaumur calibrations with the usual words: Fever Heat, Blood Heat, Summer Heat, Temperate and Freezing. The maker's or retailer's name engraved on the plates is 'C. G. Brander & Son, 82 Minories, London'.

The cases for this type of barometer varied from maker to maker with the pediments being either round top, carved or square moulded. The carving above the cistern also varied in form, with some being just bow-fronted.

Fig. 230 illustrates a popular carved walnut barometer fitted with a sympiesometer in place of a thermometer. Sympiesometers are explained in chapter 12; they are a type of barometer and were used in conjunction with a marine barometer if very accurate and comparative observations were required. For marine use the tube of the sympiesometer had to be contracted to prevent oscillation. Being extremely sensitive and of convenient size, the instrument was used instead of a barometer for marine observations for a period, but owing to its tendency to be put out of adjustment in transit, it was relegated to an instrument of comparison.

Fig. 231 illustrates another Kew pattern marine barometer made by Patrick Adie around 1885. It is very similar to his barometer shown in *Fig.* 220 except that the thermometer glass has a white back and the Fahrenheit scale is engraved on the front of the thermometer glass. The barometer scale is graduated in tenths and twentieths of an inch, whilst the vernier is graduated in twenty-fifths of an inch giving an accuracy to one five-hundredths of an inch. The barometer is signed 'P. Adie, 1 Broadway, Westminster' and numbered MD 1142. He moved to this address in 1884.

A Fitzroy marine or gun marine barometer made around 1900 is illustrated in *Fig.* 232. It is almost identical to the one shown in *Fig.* 224 made some thirty-six years earlier; the difference being that it has no thermometer and Fitzroy's words have been replaced by a millimetre scale from 69 to 78 millimetres. It is mounted in a bronzed metal frame and has all the improvements to prevent the mercury pumping in bad weather, as recommended by the Brussels Conference for Marine Meteorological Observations in 1853.

In 1914 E. Gold of the Meteorological Office, London, suggested the millibar as a unit of atmospheric pressure. It was adopted by the Meteorological Office and introduced as the unit of pressure in the daily weather reports from 1 April 1914. From this date marine and station barometers were calibrated with a millibar scale in addition to the inch scale.

Fig. 233 shows a marine barometer with an inch and a millibar scale made around 1920 by Marine Instruments Ltd, Newcastle upon Tyne. The case is of brass with a steel cistern cover and there is a Fahrenheit thermometer, attached to the case, with the scale engraved on the glass tube. The inch scale is from 26 to 32 inches with a corresponding millibar scale from 880 to 1080 millibars; the vernier is calibrated in both scales.

These barometers were supplied in carrying cases of varnished deal with lock, key, rope handles and rubber interior fittings as shown in *Fig.* 234. The barometer in the case was made by Negretti & Zambra, London, around 1940 and is engraved 'Barometer Marine Mark II Ref. Met 1542'. It is also

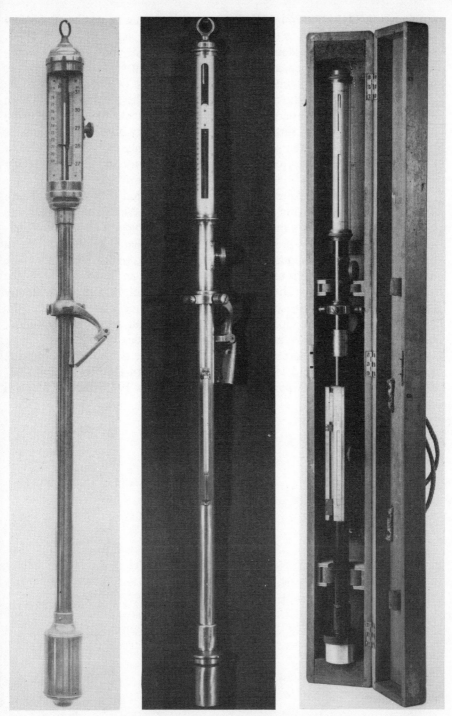

Fig. 232   Fitzroy marine or gun marine barometer. Unsigned, c. 1900.   *Fig.* 233   Kew pattern marine barometer in brass cylindrical case by Marine Instruments Ltd, Newcastle upon Tyne, c. 1920 (*M. W. Cox, Bristol*).   *Fig.* 234   Kew pattern marine barometer with a Gold Slide by Negretti & Zambra, London, c. 1940.

179

numbered 'MO. M4694/44/54/58'. This indicates that its number is M4694 and that it was returned to the makers for checking and servicing in 1944, 1954 and 1958. It has a steel cistern with a brass case and a gimbals which has a 12 inch long suspension arm to keep the instrument well clear of the wall on which it is mounted; this minimises risk of damage when the barometer swings from the movement of the ship. The glass tube has a bore of 0.315 of an inch and is contracted to 0.063 of an inch; the middle portion of the contraction is still further reduced to a capillary bore and a Bunten air trap is fitted. The silvered scale is engraved with only the millibar scale of 870 to 1100 millibars; there is a rack-operated vernier and glass protecting sheath.

Instead of an ordinary thermometer the case is fitted with a 'Gold Slide'. This is a device invented in 1914 by E. Gold of the Meteorological Office, London, and comprises a thermometer built into a type of slide rule. It has a small movable scale of latitude which is clamped with its base mark opposite the calibrated index correction of the barometer. A larger slide carries a scale of 'height above sea level' which can be adjusted, by the milled screw on the right-hand side, to make any height coincide with any latitude. It also has a scale of barometer corrections alongside the thermometer tube. The Gold Slide provides easy adjustment for latitude, height of cistern above mean sea level and mean index error.

There are various patterns of Gold Slides. This one is made by Negretti & Zambra, London around 1940. It is engraved Mark IV MO 3121/45/52/56/64 indicating that it was checked and serviced in 1945, 1952, 1956 and 1964.

9

Standard, Station and Scientific Barometers

At the same time that barometers were being developed for marine use there was a move, by the leading instrument-makers, to develop instruments with a greater accuracy to satisfy the demands of scientists, who suggested various designs. From 1774 the air pressure had been recorded twice daily at the Royal Society in Somerset House; the barometer used for this purpose was made by Jesse Ramsden and is illustrated in *Fig.* 57. It had an open cistern with an ivory index, a vernier and a bulb at the top of the tube to dilute the effect of any air or vapour that might percolate into the vacuum.

Dr J. F. Daniell (1790–1845), who was a Fellow of the Royal Society and Professor of Chemistry at King's College, London, felt that this barometer and other contemporary instruments were not sufficiently accurate, and in 1822 he designed a standard barometer which was made by John Newman and is illustrated in *Fig.* 235.

The case is made of mahogany and the cistern comprises a large mahogany bowl with the thermometer bulb dipping into the mercury; there is also an ivory float with an index mark to indicate changes in the level of the mercury in the cistern. A vernier with a length of 1½ inches is fitted to the silvered brass register plate which covers 27 to 31 inches. A table, unfortunately missing, was adjacent to the register plate; this gave the corrections to be applied to the barometer reading for differing temperatures.

The barometer and thermometer are signed 'Newman, London'. This was John Frederick Newman who was an optical, mathematical and philosophical instrument-maker from 1816 to 1860; he was the leading scientific barometer-maker of his day. He made standard and portable barometers for the Ross Antarctic expedition and his meteorological station barometers were installed throughout the British Empire.

Newman also developed in 1833 a portable iron cistern and one is used in the barometer shown in *Figs.* 236–8. His idea was to make barometers portable without having to use a cistern with a leather base as he considered that leather was not sufficiently durable. It was described as follows:

The cistern consists of two separate compartments: the top of the lower and the bottom of the upper, being perfectly flat, are pivoted closely

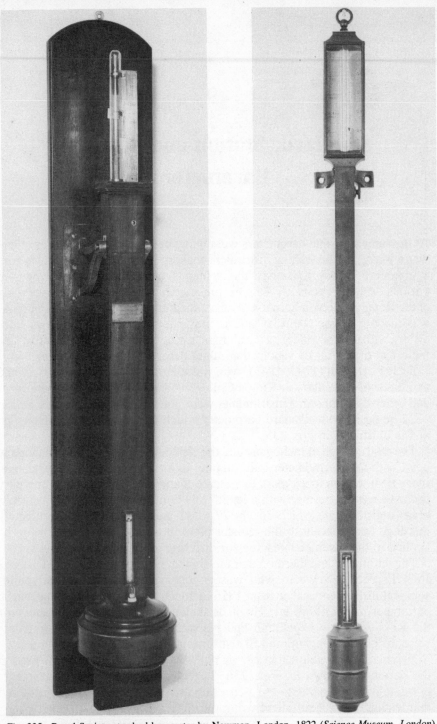

Fig. 235 Royal Society standard barometer by Newman, London, 1822 (*Science Museum, London*).
Fig. 236 Station iron cistern barometer by J. Newman, 122 Regent St, London, c. 1840.

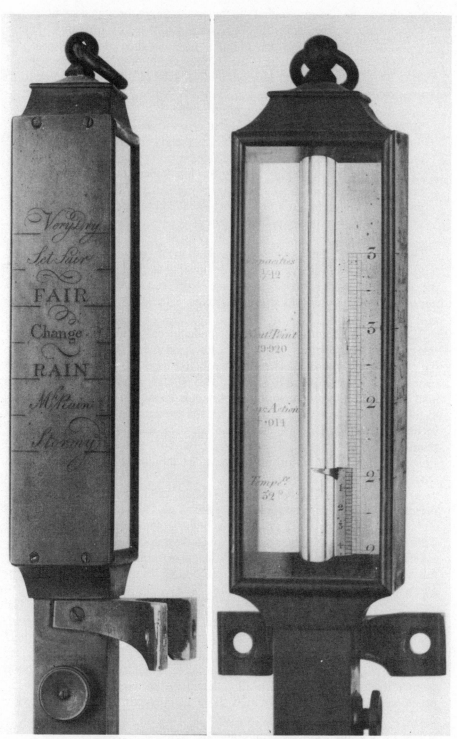

Fig. 237   Detail of *Fig. 236.*   *Fig.* 238   Detail of *Fig. 236.*

183

together at the centres, so that the lower can move through a small arc, when turned by the hand. This movement is limited by two stops. The top of the lower compartment and the bottom of the upper have each a circular hole, through which the mercury communicates. When the instrument is required for observation, the cistern is turned close up to the stop marked 'open' or 'not portable'. When it is necessary to pack it for travelling, the mercurial column must be allowed to fill the tube by sloping the barometer gently; then invert it, and move the cistern to the stop marked 'shut' or 'portable'. In this condition, the upper compartment is completely filled with mercury, and consequently that in the tube cannot move about, so as to admit air or endanger the tube. Nor can the mercury pass back to the lower compartment, as the holes are not now coincident, and the contact is made too perfect to allow the mercury to creep between the surfaces.

The case is completely made of brass with the thermometer bulb contained within the iron cistern cover. The seven weather indications are engraved on the side of the case so that prominence is given to the far more important necessary corrections which are engraved on the silvered brass register plates.

A 'Correction for Capacities 1/42' is required because the level of the mercury in the cistern varies slightly with the rise and fall of the mercury in the tube depending on the ratio between the capacity of the tube and the cistern. In this case the ratio is 1/42. The Neutral Point, 29.920 inches, is also given and indicates that no adjustment is required when the mercury is at this level. If, when taking a reading, the mercury is higher than 29.920 inches, then 1/42nd of the difference between the Neutral Point and the reading is added to the reading. When the mercury is lower than the Neutral Point then 1/42nd of the difference between the two readings is subtracted from the actual reading.

A 'Correction for Capillary Action +0.014' arises from the fact that there is capillary repulsion between mercury and glass. The surface of mercury in a glass vessel is never horizontal, but is lower at the edges than at the centre. This depression is greater in narrow tubes than in broad ones, being nearly inversely proportional to diameter. It has also been found to be greater in tubes in which the mercury has not been boiled. In this barometer 0.014 of an inch should be added to the reading.

A 'Correction for Temperature 32°' or reduction to Freezing Point. The length of the mercury column, the glass and the scale itself will vary with changes in temperature. Mercury, being a liquid, is more expansible by heat than either glass or brass and the level of the barometer will rise with any rise in temperature, even though the air pressure remains constant. To obtain comparable readings, they are all reduced to the temperature of freezing point and tables are provided which allow the correction to be applied to the observed lengths at other temperatures to reduce them to the value they would have at the standard temperature.

This barometer would have been used in meteorological stations for

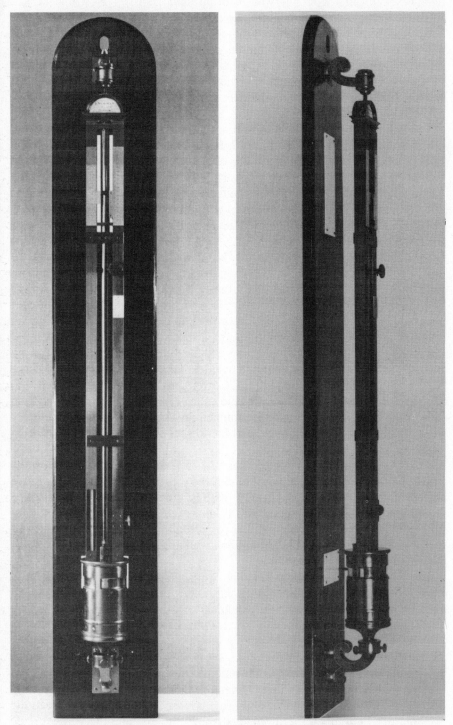

Fig. 239   Movable scale station barometer by J. Newman, 122 Regent Street, London, c. 1840 (*Negretti Automation, Aylesbury*).   *Fig.* 240   Side view of Newman barometer in *Fig.* 239.

detailed recording work. It was made around 1840 by Newman at 122 Regent Street, London, where he was working between 1827 and 1860.

Around 1840 the British Government decided to establish a number of magnetic and meteorological stations around the British Empire. Captain Edward Sabine FRS was in charge of the project and he commissioned Newman to devise a barometer as accurate as possible to be installed in each station. The outcome was the movable scale station barometer illustrated in *Figs.* 239 and 240.

The frame comprises two square brass tubes joined at the top by a domed cornice engraved 'J. Newman, 122 Regent Street, London', and at the bottom by the brass housing of the iron cistern. The construction of the cistern is identical to the two-compartment Newman cistern used for the barometer in *Fig.* 236 except that the top section of the upper compartment is made of glass so that the level of mercury in the cistern can be observed. An iron rod, tipped with an ivory point, passes through the boxwood top of the cistern so that the ivory point just touches the mercury. The other end of the rod is attached to the movable register plates. The rod can be moved up and down by a screw, on the right-hand side above the cistern, operating a rack-and-pinion mechanism. The scale, which is of platinum, can be calibrated before being attached to the barometer, and much greater accuracy can be achieved as the zero point can be adjusted by checking the position of the ivory point before taking a reading.

A thermometer has its bulb dipping into the mercury in the cistern and the tube has an inside diameter of a little over half an inch, so that it has a reasonably constant capillary correction. Corrections for capillary action and temperature are shown on the plate below the vernier screw on the right-hand side of the case. The barometer is mounted on a mahogany board with ivory plates behind the register plates, and the top section of the cistern, to make observations easier.

This movable scale barometer was regarded as the most successful and durable station barometer ever made. It was installed in all the main meteorological observatories in the British Empire. Number 58 was installed in 1841 at the Colaba Observatory, Bombay and was used every day until 1940; it had never been dismantled for cleaning or repairs. This demonstrates the very high standard of design and workmanship of John Frederick Newman.

John Benjamin Dancer appears to have specialised in station and scientific barometers at 13 Cross Street, Manchester, from 1838 to 1860. He was an optical, mathematical and philosophical instrument-maker and was in partnership with a Mr Abraham for five years from 1838.

A barometer signed by the partners is illustrated in *Fig.* 241. The case is of mahogany with the usual portable cistern and vernier, whilst all the scales are of ivory. There is a wet and dry bulb hygrometer above the cistern cover and immediately above the hygrometer is Marriott's Wet and Dry Bulb Hygrometer Table. The horizontal scale covers the difference between the wet and dry Fahrenheit thermometers from 1° to 10° and the vertical scale covers the readings of the dry thermometer from 32° to 80°. The table shows

186

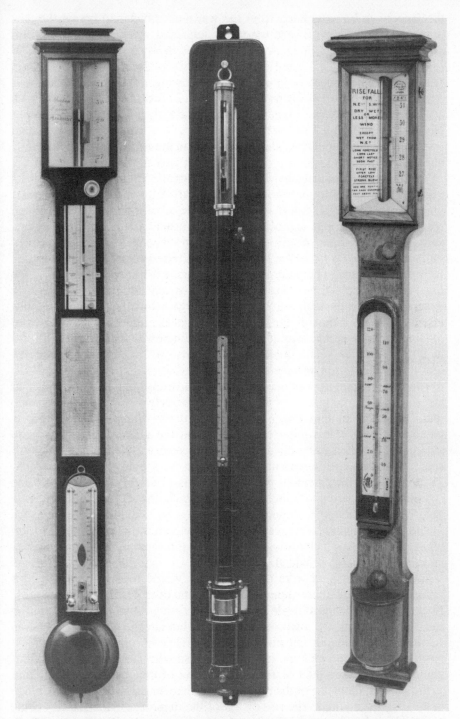

Fig. 241 Mahogany cistern barometer with wet and dry bulb hygrometer by Abraham & Dancer, Manchester, c. 1840 (*Peter D. Bosson, Wilmslow*). *Fig.* 242 Standard barometer on Fortin's principle by Chancellor & Son, Dublin, c. 1830. *Fig.* 243 Oak fishery or sea coast barometer by Negretti & Zambra, 11 Hatton Garden and Cornhill, London, 1858 (*Science Museum, London*).

the amount to be subtracted from the wet thermometer to obtain the dew point, and this figure is entered on the left-hand scale below the register plates; this scale is calibrated from 0° to 25° with 'Rain' at 0°, 'Changeable' at 6° and 'Fine' at 12°. The right-hand scale is for recording the barometer reading. From these readings accurate forecasting should be possible.

The name of Nicolas Fortin (1750–1831), a Frenchman, is associated with accurate barometers; he suggested combining a glass cistern with a leather base and an ivory point to determine the zero of the scale. This development occurred in 1809 and it had a dramatic effect on the performance of scientific barometers.

These were called standard barometers on Fortin's principle, and an example by Chancellor & Son, clockmakers of 55 Lower Sackville, Dublin, made around 1830 is shown in *Fig.* 242. The tubular metal case is painted black, with brass rings and screws, and the cistern is formed from a glass cylinder so that the level of the mercury can be seen. A conical length of ivory is fixed to the top of the inside of the cistern with the point of the cone facing downwards. The point is set to coincide exactly with the zero of the scale and before taking a reading the mercury in the cistern is raised or lowered by the adjustable screw, operating against the leather base, until it just touches the point of the ivory. This system allows a very accurate reading to be taken and was adopted and retained with little alteration for a hundred and fifty years. John Newman obviously used this idea for his movable scale station barometer (*Fig.* 239).

The upper end of the case has two vertical openings opposite each other so that readings can be taken and aided by light reflected from the white opaque glass reflector let into the mahogany board on which the barometer is mounted. There is a similar reflector behind the glass cistern so that the mercury can be adjusted accurately. The vernier allows a reading to the accuracy of one five-hundredth of an inch on the scale which extends from 27 to 33 inches. The mercury thermometer has a Fahrenheit scale, and there is a hole in the case under the thermometer bulb so that it can record more accurately the mercury temperature.

These barometers were used mainly for scientific purposes and by observatories and meteorological stations throughout the world. Glass lockable cases were provided, if required.

Standard barometers were also made that would revolve on a cast iron pedestal frame, and these were used at Kew and other leading observatories. Negretti & Zambra also made a self-compensating standard barometer; the usual form of standard instrument was used, but attached to the vernier was a double rack moved by one pinion, so that when adjusting the vernier in one position, the second rack moved in the opposite direction carrying with it a plunger dipping into the cistern. The diameter of the plunger was the same as the internal diameter of the tube so that whatever displacement took place in the cistern, owing to the rise or fall of the mercury, it was exactly compensated by the plunger being more or less immersed in the mercury. This removed the need for a correction for capacity.

A completely different type of station barometer can be attributed to

188

Admiral Fitzroy. Whilst keen to perfect the marine barometer, he was also concerned that fishermen and others, whose lives were endangered by sudden changes in the weather, should have the benefit of being able to consult a barometer. His persistence persuaded the Board of Trade in 1858 to provide, at public expense, a fishery or sea coast barometer in many fishing villages and towns, fixed in a prominent position, so that anyone wishing to consult it could do so.

Following this example, the Royal National Life Boat Institution supplied each of its stations with a similar barometer, whilst the Duke of Northumberland and the British Meteorological Society erected several on the coast of Northumberland.

Negretti & Zambra made these barometers especially for the Board of Trade and the Royal National Life Boat Institution, and *Fig.* 243 shows barometer F.B. No.2 which was issued to the St Ives Coast Guard Station in 1858. The frame is of solid oak with a strong tube of very large bore. It has a closed portable cistern, single vernier and porcelain register plates which are protected by a glazed door. The Fahrenheit thermometer scale and the register plates are signed Negretti & Zambra, under patent.

Other makers later began to produce similar barometers of inferior quality which prompted Negretti & Zambra to insert the following warning in their catalogue:

Messrs Negretti & Zambra would specially caution the Public against purchasing cheap and worthless imitations of Fishery barometers as leading to disappointment. Full details both as to construction and use of the true Fishery instrument will be found in Negretti & Zambra's Barometer Manual, compiled by Admiral Fitzroy for the Board of Trade.

Andrew Ross of Clerkenwell, London, was a reputable optical, mathematical and philosophical instrument-maker, and a fishery or sea coast barometer made by him around 1865 is illustrated in *Figs.* 244 and 245. The case is of oak with a rounded top and flat square cistern cover. The thermometer has Fahrenheit and centigrade scales and there are two verniers for comparative readings. Porcelain is used for both sets of scales and the standard correction for height is given 'Add one tenth [of an inch] for each ninety feet above the sea level'.

The weather indications on the register plates are known as Admiral Fitzroy's scale words. He realised that the standard weather indications previously used were not accurate statements of the weather conditions when taken from the level of the mercury at any particular time. He was more concerned with whether the mercury was rising or falling, the force and direction of the wind and the humidity of the atmosphere.

These barometers proved to be very successful, as is shown by an extract from Admiral Fitzroy's report from the Meteorological Office to the Board of Trade in 1864:

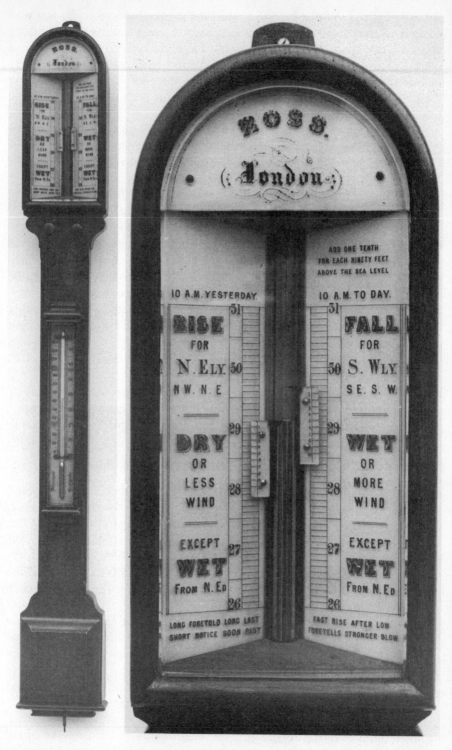

Fig. 244   Oak fishery or sea coast barometer by Ross, London, c. 1865.   *Fig.* 245   Detail of *Fig.* 244.

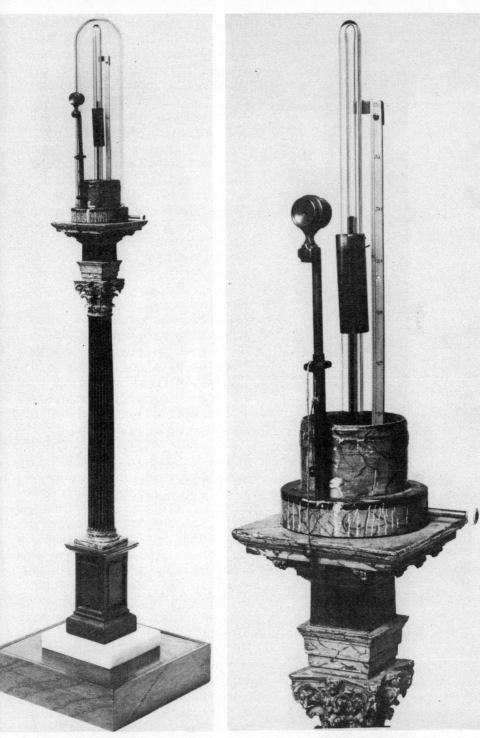

Fig. 246 Mahogany pillar barometer with low-power microscope. Unsigned, c. 1860 (*Park Street Antiques, Berkhamstead*).   *Fig.* 247 Detail of *Fig.* 246.

In my last report I stated how highly the Board of Trade 'Fishery' Barometers have been valued on the coasts. They are now eighty in all, specially lent, under due control and care. Two only of this number have become slightly defective, and have been exchanged. Not one has been injured in carriage, singular to say, between Cornwall and the Shetland Isles, Ireland and Yorkshire. It may be more readily estimated mentally than accurately proved, to what extent these simple instruments (all reliably made and tested) have already been the means of saving life and property. Explanatory manuals and blank forms for diagrams have been extensively circulated among the coasters and fishermen, who are all, now, much influenced by, and very thankful for, the benefits of this Act of their Government. Many are the local instances of similar beneficence by individuals − especially the Duke of Northumberland, who has placed no less than fourteen barometers.

In 1863 Admiral Fitzroy published his *Weather Book* which summarised his considerable work on meteorology. He also set up a series of weather stations which would telegraph weather data to the Meteorological Office in London. Using this information he produced some of the first weather charts and began issuing weather forecasts. By 1861 *The Times* was printing daily weather forecasts and Fitzroy was gaining recognition as the man who could predict coming weather conditions.

Unfortunately, Fitzroy had a number of opponents, and some of his critics wanted general theories of the science of meteorology established before weather predictions were made public. In the middle of this controversy his mind became unbalanced and, sadly, he took his own life in 1865 when he was aged 60.

Fig. 248 School laboratory siphon tube barometer. Unsigned, c. 1900.

192

Figs. 246 and 247 illustrate a scientific instrument of around 1860 by an unknown maker. A Corinthian column of mahogany is mounted on a plinth; the capital and base are of brass and the section above the column is painted and gilded. The top of the tube, scale and vernier are protected by a glass dome and the vernier adjustment screw can be seen on the right-hand side of the platform. For accurate readings a low-power microscope is mounted outside the glass dome.

A school laboratory siphon tube barometer is shown in *Fig.* 248 made around the turn of the century. It was probably for use by school pupils, in science and chemistry laboratories, solely for the purpose of measuring atmospheric pressure. The tube is of the same bore throughout its length and the boxwood scale is calibrated in centimetres and millimetres from zero to 80 centimetres. Before taking a reading, the zero on the scale is set in line with the mercury in the short limb by turning the screw on the right-hand side of the frame.

The mercury thermometer has a Fahrenheit paper scale contained within a sealed tube. This type of thermometer will float upright in a liquid and was probably detached from time to time and used to take the temperature of liquids.

10

Mountain and Balloonist's Barometers

Soon after the barometer was invented it was realised that air pressure decreased with height, and as early as 1648 Florin Perier took a barometer up the Puy-de-Dôme; he left a similar barometer at the base in Clermont with an observer and found that the mercury in the tube decreased as he climbed the mountain, whilst there was no change in air pressure in Clermont. However, it took more than a hundred years to establish a mathematical relationship between height and air pressure accurately enough to consider the barometer an acceptable instrument for measuring differences in height.

The two main problems were accuracy and portability and it was Jean André de Luc (1727–1817) who devised a portable barometer for use by travellers. He was born in Geneva and was responsible for various improvements to the barometer in the eighteenth century. In 1755 he devised a siphon-type tube, with an ivory stopcock in the short limb of the tube, so that when the tube was tilted and the long tube filled with mercury it could be locked in this position, thus preventing air entering the tube and also eliminating pumping of the mercury when the barometer was in transit. A siphon or bent tube works on the same principle as the bulb cistern tube, but the siphon tube has a uniform bore throughout its length. De Luc also introduced an unusual type of barometer scale which was calibrated up and down from a zero point near the top of the short limb; this was because it was easier to add than to subtract.

Fig. 249 illustrates a mountain barometer made by Nairne & Blunt, London, around 1785 using de Luc's principles. The case is of mahogany and the siphon tube has an ivory tap at the lower end of the short limb; it also has an ivory stopper. The silvered brass upper register plate is calibrated 15 to 23 in Paris inches, whilst the lower plate is calibrated down from 1 to 8 Paris inches; the two readings added together give the height of the mercury. The thermometer on the left records the temperature of the barometer, whilst the thermometer on the right can be removed from the case and used to measure the ambient temperature. Its removal also allows the short limb to be cleaned with the swab attached to the wire on the door of the case. There is a plumb bob, protected from wind by a glazed door, above the thermometer, so that the instrument can be positioned vertically before a reading is taken.

A mountain barometer made around the same time by John Miller of

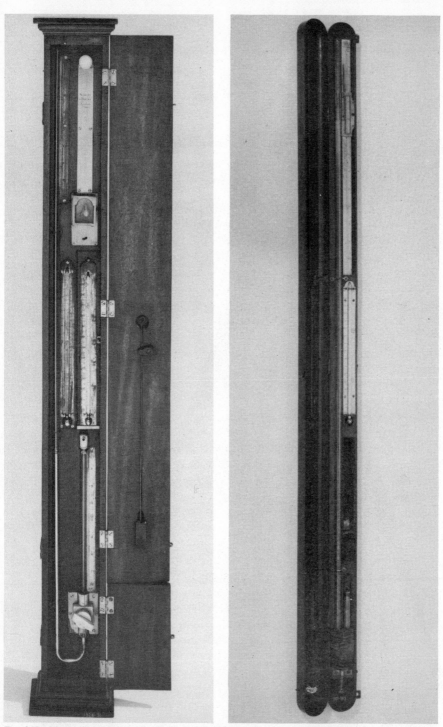

Fig. 249 Mountain barometer on de Luc's principle by Nairne & Blunt, London, c. 1785 (*Science Museum, London*). *Fig.* 250 Mountain barometer by J. Miller, Edinburgh, c. 1785 (*Science Museum, London*).

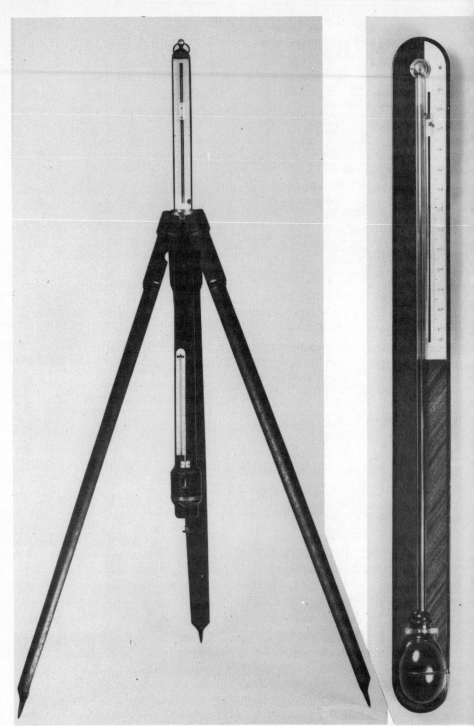

Fig. 251   Mountain barometer with ivory float and tripod by Nairne & Blunt, c. 1790 (*Bert Bolle, Holland*).   *Fig.* 252   Extended scale mahogany cistern barometer by Blunt & Son, London, c. 1805 (*Stair & Co. Ltd, London*).

Edinburgh is shown in *Fig.* 250. It is contained in a mahogany case with a portable cistern tube of the bellows type used exclusively by Scottish makers. The silvered brass register plate extends from 19 to 32 inches, divided into twentieths of an inch, and the vernier is operated manually by turning a cogged wheel on the vernier which engages a series of teeth along the register plate. An instrument is missing below the Fahrenheit thermometer; it could have been a plug or float for the short glass tube set in the top of the cistern.

John Miller served an apprenticeship in the workshops in London of George Adams senior; he returned to Edinburgh and set up in business on his own in 1771 as an optical, mathematical and philosophical instrument-maker. He was an uncle of Alexander Adie whom he took as an apprentice and made a partner in 1804, when they traded as Miller & Adie.

Mountain barometers were also made using portable cisterns and ivory floats, but they were much reduced in size and weight to make carrying easier. Before a reading could be taken the barometer had to be in an exactly vertical position and to achieve this a tripod had to be used. An innovation, believed to have been suggested by Jesse Ramsden, was to use the tripod as a carrying case for the barometer by hollowing out the legs sufficiently to contain the tube and cistern.

An example of this type of mountain barometer is given in *Fig.* 251. The case and tripod are of solid mahogany and there is a brass gimbals to allow the instrument to remain upright. The cistern has a portable screw and ivory float and the thermometer bulb is housed within the cistern cover. The silvered brass register plates were originally engraved in English inches but the barometer was later exported to France and the plates re-engraved with Paris inches on the right-hand side and centimetres on the left-hand side. The legs of the tripod are hollowed to contain the barometer in transit. The maker was Nairne & Blunt, London, around 1790.

The barometer illustrated in *Fig.* 252 by Blunt & Son is identical to the barometer shown in *Fig.* 124 by Blunt, London, except that it has the scale extended from 17 to 29 inches. This raises the question whether it was intended for domestic, mountain or mountain station use. The case is veneered with mahogany in the herring-bone style and the edges have an ebonised banding. The cistern is not portable and the typical Blunt egg-shaped cistern cover is used. There is no thermometer and the scale implies that it was only intended to be used between 2,000 and 14,000 feet above sea level. The instrument is not truly portable or particularly accurate, but it is known that Thomas Blunt was interested in altitude and devised some of the features of Magellan's 'New Barometer' for measuring heights. Perhaps Blunt fitted an extended scale to one of his domestic barometers for experimental purposes.

The majority of mountain barometers were made using the Fortin-type cistern and an illustration is given in *Fig.* 253. The case is made completely of brass and the scale is calibrated from 16 to 33 inches, giving it a range of 15,000 feet. A vernier is operated by the screw at the top of the case and the thermometer has Fahrenheit and centigrade scales. The mahogany travelling

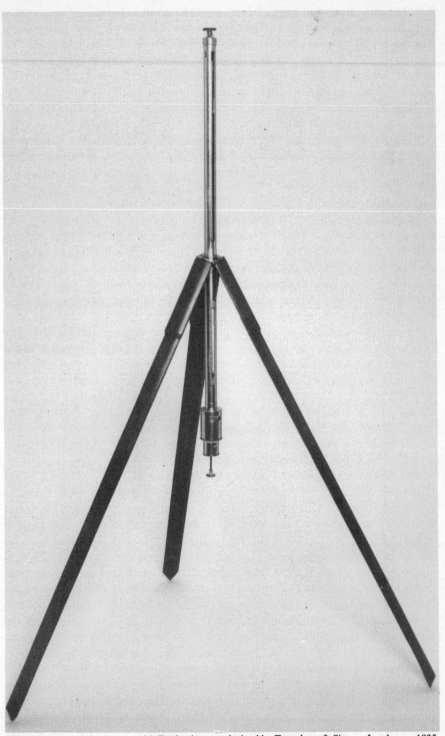

Fig. 253 Mountain barometer with Fortin cistern and tripod by Troughton & Simms, London, c. 1835
(*Sotheby's, London*).

Fig. 254 Newman's improved portable iron cistern mountain barometer by J. Newman, 122 Regent Street, London, c. 1840 (*Meteorological Office, Bracknell*). *Fig.* 255 Detail of *Fig.* 254. *Fig.* 256 Detail of *Fig.* 254.

case divides to form a tripod stand incorporating gimbals with a height of 43 inches when closed.

'Troughton & Simms, London' is engraved on the cistern cover above the opening to view the mercury in the glass cistern. This was a partnership between Edward Troughton and William Simms (1793–1860) formed in 1826. Troughton retired in 1831 but the business continued until, eventually, Cooke, Troughton and Simms Ltd was taken over by Vickers Instruments Ltd.

It has already been said that John Frederick Newman was the leader in the development of the station barometer; he was also responsible for the Newman mountain barometer illustrated in *Figs*. 254–6. The case is of mahogany and there is a brass shield, which slides round to the scale part of the frame, to protect it and the tube when in transit. The silvered brass register plate extends from 18.5 to 32 inches and the scales are divided into twentieths of an inch; the vernier is also divided into twentieths of an inch and is operated by the screw at the top of the instrument. The two-compartment iron cistern invented by Newman, and already referred to, is used and has 'portable' and 'not portable' positions. *Fig*. 256 shows the bulb of the thermometer to be within the cistern cover and the barometer tube can just be seen above the scale.

The ivory plate round the barometer below the register plate is engraved 'Newman's Improved Portable Iron Cistern, 122 Regent Street, London'. It also gives the corrections for capacity, neutral point, capillary action and temperature. It was made around 1840 and called 'Improved' because it incorporated his two-compartment iron cistern which he introduced in 1833 as an improvement on his earlier single-compartment iron cistern, developed in 1823.

Newman's mountain barometers could, of course, also be used by balloonists but as they were generally only calibrated down to 20 inches they could not be used for altitudes much above 10,000 feet.

A balloonist's barometer calibrated from 15 to 33 inches, which gives it a range of up to 16,000 feet, is illustrated in *Fig*. 257. The case is of mahogany and the silvered brass register plate has two verniers which are both operated by the screw on the right-hand side below the plate. One vernier covers the top half of the scale and the other the lower half; two are necessary because the scale is more than half the length of the case and if only one was used the rackwork would extend beyond the bottom of the case when taking readings below 19 inches.

The mercury thermometer has a Fahrenheit scale and there is a temperature correction table engraved on the ivory plate round the case below the vernier screw. It is headed 'Correction for Expansion of Mercury and Mean Dilatation of Glass'. There are two scales: a vertical scale headed 'Temperature of Mercury in Fahrenheit' from 25+ to 70− in steps of 5, and a horizontal scale headed 'Height of Mercury in Inches' from 28 to 31½ inches in half-inch steps. The thermometer falls about one degree for each 300 feet of elevation from the ground, but varies with wind.

A portable boxwood cistern is used with the adjustable screw contained

200

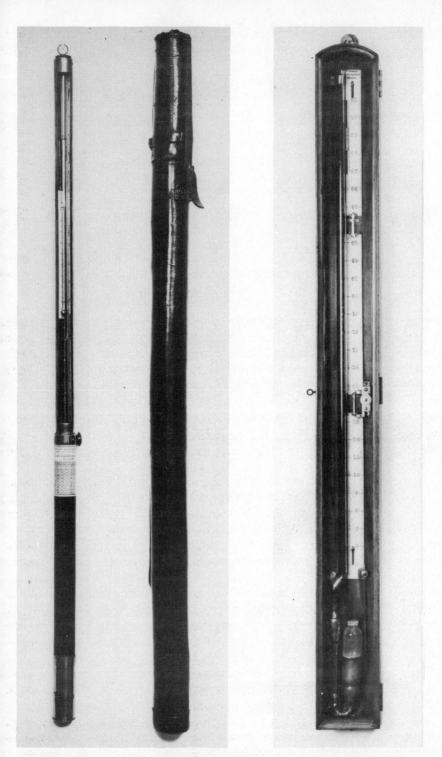

Fig. 257   Balloonist's mahogany barometer with travelling case by Thomas Jones, London, c. 1840
(*Derek Rayment Antiques, Barton*).   *Fig.* 258   Balloonist's barometer in a mahogany case by
H. Negretti, 19 Leather Lane, Holborn, c. 1845.

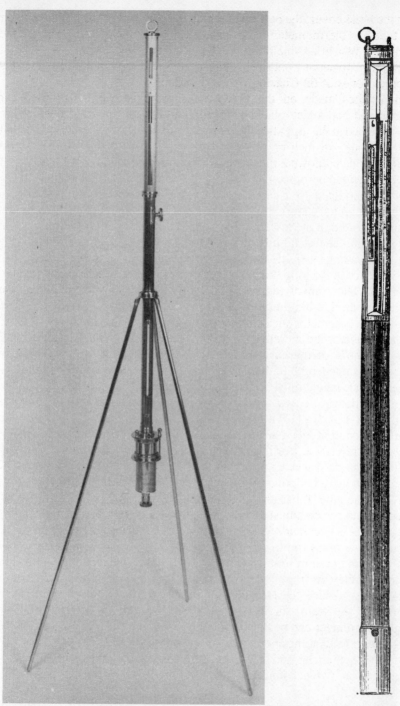

Fig. 259   Fortin principle mountain barometer with brass case and tripod. Inch and millimetre scales by Gapp, London, c. 1870 (*Park Street Antiques, Berkhamstead*).   *Fig.* 260   Line drawing of Newman's mountain barometer in turned mahogany frame, having brass shield and portable screw. Detachable thermometer on silvered brass scale from Negretti & Zambra's catalogue 1878.

within the brass cover, the bottom of which unscrews for access. The register plate, tube and thermometer can be protected, when being transported in the leather case, by a brass shield that can be rotated to cover them. The maker's name, 'Thos. Jones of London', is engraved on the thermometer scale; this is Thomas Jones of 62 Charing Cross, London.

Siphon tubes made on the Gay-Lussac principle were also used for mountain and balloonist's barometers. In this design the short limb of the tube was sealed at the top, after the mercury had been introduced, and a small hole was made, an inch or so below the seal, which was covered with a substance which allowed the access of air but prevented the escape of mercury when the barometer was packed for travelling. The bent part of the tube was contracted to a capillary bore so that when the barometer was inverted the capillary attraction kept the mercury in the long limb. A Bunten air trap was fitted in the lower end of the long limb to prevent any air rising to the vacuum. The metal tube protecting the glass was graduated from the centre and readings were taken from two verniers, one positioned at the top of the mercury in the long limb and the other at the top of the mercury in the short limb. The sum of the two readings gave the correct height of the mercury to one five-hundredth of an inch.

The siphon barometer does not require correction for capillary or capacity, as each surface of the mercury is equally depressed by capillary attraction, and the quantity of mercury which falls from the long limb of the tube occupies the same length in the short limb, as the diameter of both are equal. The barometric height must, however, be corrected for temperature as in the cistern barometer.

J. L. Gay-Lussac (1778–1850) was a famous French chemist who favoured the siphon tube barometer, and in 1816 improved its performance in the ways described. For the following seventy years it was popular with travellers because it was light and compact.

Fig. 258 shows a balloonist's barometer by H. Negretti which uses a type of Gay-Lussac tube. It has an ivory scale which is calibrated from 31 inches to 5 inches and can be adjusted by turning the ivory circular key half way up the tube. This is necessary to zero the scale by ensuring that the brass arm, connected by a brass rod to the bottom of the scale, is level with the top of the mercury in the short limb. The bulge in the lower section of the long limb contains a Bunten air trap. The case is made of mahogany with a glazed door and the maker's name 'H. Negretti, 19 Leather Lane, Holborn' is engraved at the top of the scale. As he only occupied these premises from 1843 to 1848, the barometer can be dated to within five years. Henry Negretti came to England in 1830 at the age of 12 and was apprenticed to F. A. Pizzala, an optical, mathematical and philosophical instrument-maker. He was in business on his own account by 1840 and formed a partnership with J. W. Zambra in 1850.

This instrument has a vernier which only covers the normal scale of 27 to 31 inches which suggests that its main purpose was that of an ordinary barometer. However, it can record altitudes of up to 40,000 feet – almost 8 miles – and was probably used for early balloon experiments, since Henry

203

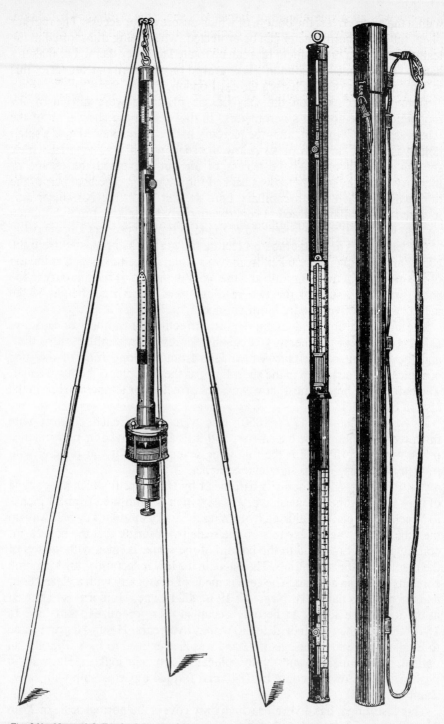

Fig. 261 Negretti & Zambra's mountain barometer on Fortin's principle with brass tripod stand from their catalogue 1878. *Fig.* 262 Standard siphon tube mountain barometer on Gay-Lussac's principle with leather travelling case from Negretti & Zambra's catalogue 1878.

Negretti was an acquaintance of James Glaisher, the well-known balloon pioneer. It is known that Glaisher compared two of Negretti & Zambra's aneroid barometers with a siphon tube mercury barometer at pressures down to 7 inches, and this could well have been the barometer used. He made numerous risky meteorological hot-air balloon ascents and on one flight, while testing the composition of the air at 37,000 feet, was almost asphyxiated.

Fig. 262 shows a standard siphon tube mountain barometer, on Gay-Lussac's principle, taken from the 1878 catalogue of Negretti & Zambra. It has a brass tubular case on which the scale graduations are engraved, with one vernier at the top of the long limb and another at the bottom of the short limb, reading from the centre. By adding the two readings together the correct height of the mercury is obtained to one five-hundredths of an inch. There is a thermometer for temperature correction and the tube is fitted with a Bunten air trap. This barometer sold for eight guineas in 1878 with a brass tripod stand and leather travelling case.

11

Double- and Multiple-tube Barometers

Although mercury has the great advantage of compactness and a low heat expansion ratio, a large number of experiments were carried out with other liquids in an endeavour to make the barometer more easily readable by magnifying the scale. The liquids used were water, olive oil, linseed oil, glycerine and sulphuric acid, but all of these had various disadvantages.

Fig. 6 (in chapter 1) shows a water barometer built by Robert Boyle outside his house in 1669. The tube was made of tinned iron with a glass section near the top to view the level of the water, but, as can be seen, it was a very cumbersome instrument extending to between 30 and 40 feet. Another disadvantage was that water, and other liquids, slowly evaporated and their volume changed appreciably with changes in temperature. The liquid and the inside of the tube became very dirty from constant contact with the air.

The outcome was a compromise by using mercury in conjunction with a second liquid and this development is attributed to Robert Hooke (1635–1703) who, in 1668, demonstrated a 'Double Barometer' to the Royal Society. He was the son of a clergyman and became a brilliant engineer, inventing the wheel barometer and the air pump in its enduring form. It is said that he added something to every important instrument developed in the seventeenth century and has been called the founder of scientific meteorology.

A double barometer using the type of tube invented by Robert Hooke is shown in *Figs.* 263 and 264. The double tube is approximately 43 inches long, with the left-hand tube sealed and the right-hand tube open. The left-hand tube is filled with mercury, as in a siphon tube, up to the centre of the bulb in the right-hand tube and an oil is added to this tube which is calibrated from 0 to 100 upwards; the actual scale covers 30 inches which gives a magnification of 10. The mercury can carry the much less dense oil without affecting its operation appreciably, and the difference between the surface areas of the bulb cistern and the open tube gives the magnification. The scale is, of course, reversed as an increase in pressure pushes the oil further down the open tube; for this reason the instrument is sometimes referred to as a 'contra-barometer'.

The case is of mahogany with carved decoration, whilst the scale is of boxwood which is headed 'The Great Double Barometer' and ornamented with a wheat-ear border and symmetrical designs. The tube is not protected

Fig. 263　Great double barometer in carved mahogany case. Unsigned, c. 1760.　　*Fig.* 264　Detail of
Fig. 263.

by glass and there is a manually operated pointer on a brass wire. The barometer is unsigned and was probably made around 1760.

Very few of this type of barometer appear to have been made during the eighteenth century, but they were far more popular on the Continent, particularly in Holland, where they were called contra-barometers. However, quite a number were made in Scotland at the end of the century and this was probably on the initiative of Balthazar Knie who arrived in Edinburgh from Europe in 1776 and brought the design with him.

A double barometer signed 'Knie Edin^r' and made around 1790 is illustrated in *Fig.* 265. The mahogany case has a scroll pediment with a full length glazed door, the frame of which is veneered with mahogany and kingwood. The indicating tube is on the left-hand side of the silvered brass register plate which is calibrated 150 at Stormy 28 inches, 100 at Much Rain, 50 at Rain 29 inches, 0 at Change, 50 at Fair 30 inches, 100 at Set Fair and 150 at Very Dry 31 inches.

Fig. 266 shows a double barometer with a thermometer, made by T. Thomson of Edinburgh around 1805. The mahogany case is very similar to the Knie barometer case, just described, except that there are mahogany, boxwood and ebonised inlays, also stringing round the silvered brass register plate and glazed door frame. The barometer calibrations are identical to those of the Knie instrument, but the case is wider to house the spirit thermometer between the barometer limbs. The Fahrenheit scale is unusually annotated 'Agreeable' at 64°. The barometer reading indicator, which operates manually in a groove, does not have a vernier.

'Double Barometer' is engraved at the top of the register plate and 'Thermometer' is also engraved in a cartouche above the tube; between the two is another cartouche with 'T. Thomson, Edin.' engraved. This was Thomas Thomson who described himself as a glassblower in the Cowgate, Edinburgh; he was working there between 1805 and 1809.

A double barometer of the Art Nouveau period is illustrated in *Fig.* 267. The frame is of mahogany and the barometer and thermometer scales are made of white opaque glass. The barometer has inch and millimetre scales, whilst the thermometer scale covers Fahrenheit and centigrade. The instrument is made portable by a tap near the base of the right-hand limb; this is closed when the barometer is inclined and the left-hand limb is full of mercury.

The top plate is worded 'Contra Barometer 610', and there is an ivory plate giving the maker's description 'Otto Baumbach, Maker of Scientific Apparatus (Glass Blower by Appointment to the University of Manchester) 10 Lime Grove, Oxford Road, Manchester'. It was made around 1900.

Various attempts were made, in the seventeenth century and later, to improve the portability of the mercury barometer by reducing its size. With this in mind Guillaume Amontons in 1688 suggested splitting the height of the mercury column by joining together several parallel tubes and filling them alternately with mercury and a lighter liquid. This design was followed by a number of Italian makers and it became known as the double or multiple-tube barometer.

Fig. 265 Double barometer in mahogany case by Knie, Edinburgh, c. 1790 (*Mallett & Son (Antiques) Ltd, London*). *Fig.* 266 Double barometer and thermometer in mahogany case by T. Thomson, Edinburgh, c. 1805. *Fig.* 267 Contra-barometer and thermometer on mahogany frame by Otto Baumbach, Manchester, c. 1905.

Fig. 268 Double or multiple-tube barometer in mahogany case by Bapt. Roncheti & Co., c. 1785.
Fig. 269 Bapt. Roncheti & Co. barometer, with door open.

An example by Bapt. Roncheti & Co., which can be dated about 1785, is given in *Figs*. 268 and 269. The case is made of mahogany with a glazed door; the finials are of brass and the thermometer scales and weather indications are printed on paper, decorated with pillars festooned with leaves, flowers and fruit and capped with masonic signs, birds and human figures.

Mercury and oil are used alternately in the tubes and the level of the oil in the open right-hand side tube indicates the atmospheric pressure; the lower the pressure the higher the oil rises in the tube. The scale is calibrated down from 50 'Stormy' to 0 'Very Dry'. The spirit thermometer has a Fahrenheit scale. The barometer is 24 inches high, and by using oil in conjunction with mercury the scale is extended to 15 inches as against 3 inches for the normal stick barometer.

A similar barometer by Rabalio made about ten years later is shown in *Fig*. 270. The main difference is that the thermometer scales and weather indications are stamped on a boxwood base. It also has a set hand that slides up and down a brass wire which is secured at the top and bottom of the door frame.

This type of barometer was also made by James Gatty, Dominick Manticha, Dominico Sala, Charles Silberrad and Torre. It never became popular and was made for only a short period, the main disadvantages being that the liquids could easily become intermingled when the barometer was carried or shaken; the tubes also become stained and are difficult to clean.

A water barometer with a glass tube 40 feet in length and of one inch internal diameter was constructed by Professor J. F. Daniell of King's College in 1830 for the Royal Society at Somerset House. The cistern was in the form of a small steam boiler, so that the water, previously distilled, could be freed from air by boiling and immediately put into the tube. When the Royal Society vacated Somerset House the barometer was moved to the Crystal Palace, but was destroyed by fire in 1866. A replacement water barometer was erected by J. B. Jordan but it was not very satisfactory as in 1880 he wrote:

Although the water barometer is an instrument of much interest as a weather glass, it is found to be of little value for indicating with certainty the variations in atmospheric pressure, owing to the effect of temperature on the aqueous vapour above the column: this fact led to the examination of other fluids than water for the barometric column, and among those tried glycerine appears to be the best suited for the purpose.

He was given a grant of £30 to set up a glycerine barometer at Kew Observatory, and Mr Whipple, the director at Kew, stated that the records obtained by it were fairly satisfactory. The movement of a glycerine column is 10.76 times greater than that of a mercurial column, at the standard temperature, as 333.57 inches of glycerine are equal to 31 inches of mercury. It was considered a reasonable success as at least eight similar barometers were erected elsewhere.

211

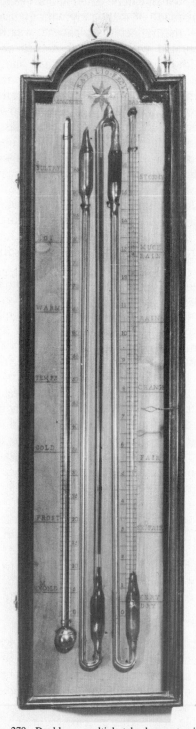
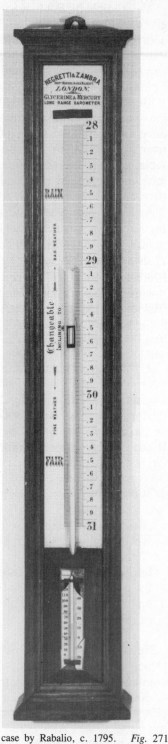

Fig. 270 Double or multiple-tube barometer in mahogany case by Rabalio, c. 1795. *Fig.* 271
Glycerine and mercury long-range barometer by Negretti & Zambra, London, c. 1885.

With a tube length of 27 feet, Jordan's barometer could only be installed in very few buildings and this prompted Negretti & Zambra to develop a new long range mercurial and glycerine barometer in the early 1880s. It was also called the long range or open scale barometer and an illustration is given in *Fig.* 271.

The case is made of oak and at the bottom there is a mercury thermometer with a Fahrenheit and centigrade scale. A siphon tube is used with the closed end about 33 inches long and the other only a few inches in length; to this short end is joined a glass tube of much smaller diameter so that both limbs are the same length with the smaller one being open at the top. The large tube, which is behind the porcelain register plate and cannot be seen, is filled with mercury, and the small tube, which is broken, is partly filled with glycerine. Due to the unequal capacity of the two tubes and the difference in the specific gravity of mercury and glycerine, the scale is extended over 24 inches or 8 times a normal mercury scale; this makes it possible to take readings to one-hundredth of an inch without the use of a vernier. The register plate is headed 'Negretti & Zambra, Instrument Makers to Her Majesty, London. Glycerine & Mercury Long Range Barometer'. It was made around 1885 and sold for six guineas; this included an iron stopcock for making the instrument portable in transit.

12

Sympiesometers

The sympiesometer was invented and patented by Alexander Adie in 1818. The patent was entitled 'An Improvement on the air barometer' and it was, in fact, an improvement of Robert Hooke's thermobarometer which he described in a paper he presented to the Royal Society in 1668.

This was the same type of instrument advertised by John Patrick in his advertisement shown in *Fig.* 25 (chapter 2), numbered 2, and described as 'A Ship Barometer' 'A Foot Long'. An outline of this thermobarometer is given at the beginning of chapter 8.

A sympiesometer made by Adie around 1825 is illustrated in *Fig.* 272. The case is of mahogany with a full-length glazed door and a height of a little over 24 inches. The top part of the tube, including the closed bulb, is filled with hydrogen, whilst the lower part of the tube and the open bulb contains a coloured almond oil. There is a fixed scale of temperatures on the extreme right of the case, and a scale of pressures is made to slide against it.

As hydrogen is affected by both pressure and temperature of the atmosphere, it is necessary to adjust for the temperature before taking a reading. To do this the thermometer on the left is first read and an index mark on the scale of pressures is set opposite the reading on the fixed scale of temperatures by raising or lowering the sliding scale with the brass knob outside the case. The pressure is then read from the sliding scale opposite the level of the oil in the tube. There is a circular recording dial at the bottom of the case.

The word sympiesometer means 'compressed measure' and its advantage was that it was smaller and simpler than the mercury barometer. It was developed primarily by Adie to replace the marine barometer and he arranged for it to be tested extensively on board ship, both in arctic and tropical conditions, before applying for a patent. The Commander of HMS *Isabella,* one of the ships on the Ross expedition to the Arctic, is said to have written:

> The Sympiesometer is a most excellent instrument and shows the weather far better than the marine barometer. In short, the barometer is of no use compared to it . . . in my opinion it surpasses the mercurial barometer as much as the barometer is superior to having none at all.

Alexander Adie (1774–1858) was an optical, mathematical and

214

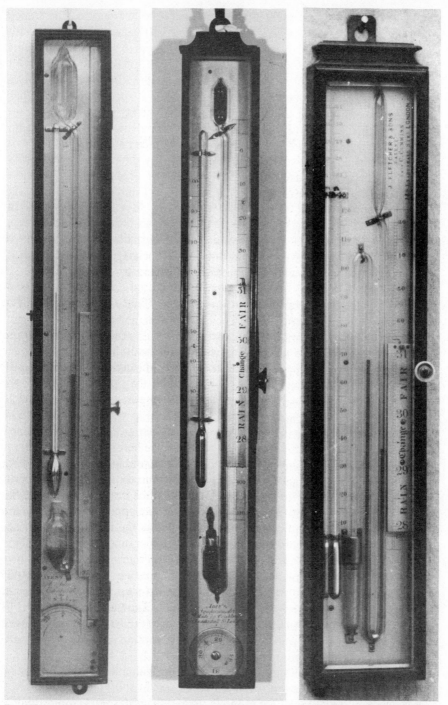

Fig. 272   Sympiesometer in mahogany case by A. Adie, Edinburgh, No. 537, c. 1825.   *Fig.* 273
Adie's marine sympiesometer in mahogany case by Crichton, 112 Leadenhall Street, London, c. 1840
(*Dreweatt Watson & Barton, Newbury*).   *Fig.* 274   Sympiesometer in mahogany case by J. Fletcher &
Sons, Patent, Late C. Cummins, 148 Leadenhall Street, London, c. 1845 (*Peter D. Bosson, Wilmslow*).

215

philosophical instrument-maker who was very highly regarded; he traded from various addresses in Edinburgh between 1804 and 1858. He and his second son John were the only two instrument-makers to be elected members of the Royal Society of Edinburgh.

Adie numbered his sympiesometers and the silvered brass register plates are engraved 'Patent. A. Adie Edinburgh No. 537'. It appears that more than 2,500 were made by Adie and his son John over the sixty years following the granting of the patent; in London he used Spencer Browning & Rust as his agent and it is calculated that about 90 were produced annually for the first fifteen years when the instrument was protected by the patent, followed by 30 a year when other makers were allowed to copy them.

Adie died in 1858 and the Royal Society of Edinburgh recorded the following tribute to him:

Mr. Alexander Adie's . . . attention to business, with his skills as a mechanic, his quick inventive powers, led to his being employed by all kinds of inventors, to give their schemes a practical form . . . .

A similar sympiesometer made around 1840 by Crichton, when the patent had expired, is shown in *Fig.* 273. The case is of mahogany and the register plates are of silvered brass. This instrument was made specifically for marine use as it has a constriction in the tube opposite the top of the open bulb; this prevents violent oscillations of the liquid caused by the motion of the ship.

Above the air pressure recording wheel is engraved 'Adie's Sympiesometer. Made by Crichton, 122 Leadenhall Street, London'. This was Joseph Crichton, an instrument-maker who also made barometers between 1838 and 1851.

A disadvantage of using hydrogen and oil was that the oil ·gradually absorbed the hydrogen, and by the process of osmosis the light gas escaped over a period, whilst the remainder became mixed with air. The thermal lag of the bulb of hydrogen was also much less than that of the mercury thermometer and this prompted J. D. Forbes (1809–68), an eminent Scottish scientist, to suggest that the bulb of the thermometers should be placed inside the hydrogen bulb.

In 1840 Charles Cummins was granted a patent for a sympiesometer using sulphuric acid instead of almond oil. An instrument made by J. Fletcher & Sons, of 148 Leadenhall Street, London, under the patent is illustrated in *Fig.* 274. The case is of mahogany and the double tube contains coloured sulphuric acid in the lower bulb and in the recording section. There is a manually operated recording scale at the top left-hand side of the silvered brass register plates. J. Fletcher appears to have taken over the business of Charles Cummins in Leadenhall St on his death.

Another patent was taken out by A. O. Harris in 1850 for a sympiesometer using carbon dioxide as the gas and mercury as the liquid. These were made by the firm William Harris & Son of 50 High Holborn, London, and an illustration is given in *Fig.* 275. The silvered brass register plate is engraved

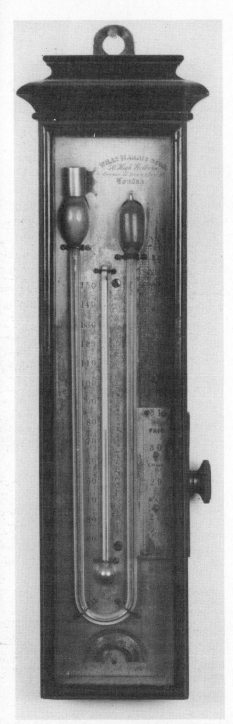

Fig. 275   Harris's patent compensating portable barometer No. 258 by William Harris & Son, 50 High Holborn, London, c. 1855 (*Christies, London*).   *Fig.* 276   Improved marine sympiesometer in glazed ebony case by Owens, South Castle Street, Liverpool, c. 1860 (*Phillips, London*).

Fig. 277   Pocket sympiesometer with ivory register plate, 6 inches high, by English, Brighton, c. 1865 (*Science Museum, London*).   *Fig.* 278   Improved marine sympiesometer in glazed mahogany case by J. Hughes, Ratcliff, London, c. 1870.   *Fig.* 279   Sympiesometer/clock/thermometer in rosewood case and with ivory plates. Unsigned, c. 1880 (*M. & S. Cumper Ltd, South Newton*).

'Harris's Patent Compensating Portable Barometer' and numbered 258. The case is of rosewood and there is a mercury thermometer and sliding barometric scale. Overall, the instrument is only 13 inches in height.

Very few of the Cummins and Harris type instruments appear to have been made, with the result that they are now very rare, but a large number of 'Improved Sympiesometers' were produced between 1860 and 1890. An example is given in *Fig.* 276 made by Owens, South Castle Street, Liverpool, around 1860.

It is in a glazed ebony case 19¼ inches high and is called 'Improved' because air and sulphuric acid are used in place of hydrogen and oil. The upper portion of the tube is filled with air, whilst the lower portion and part of the cistern are filled with sulphuric acid, coloured to make it visible. The cistern is open at the top through a kind of pipette or cone, and a brass cover prevents dust and dirt from entering the tube. An adjustable scale of pressures is mounted over a fixed scale of temperatures and before a reading is taken the pointer attached to the top of the pressure scale is adjusted to the appropriate temperature by the brass slide outside the case. This sympiesometer was made for use at sea as it has a contraction in the tube opposite the cistern; this prevents oscillation of the liquid.

The size of the sympiesometer varied between 6 and 24 inches in height depending on the purpose for which the instrument was required. The smallest was the pocket instrument as illustrated in *Fig.* 277. It is 6 inches in height with an ivory register plate and protected by a velvet-lined pasteboard. There is a manually operated adjustable scale of pressures and a Fahrenheit thermometer. It is described as a pocket barometer and the maker or retailer is English, Brighton.

This type of sympiesometer was also made in morocco leather hinged cases, suitable for travelling and for the pocket. Others were made for climbers or for taking altitudes of up to 10,000 and 15,000 feet; these had leather sling cases.

Although the sympiesometer was said to be portable, it had to be carried and handled so as to keep it more or less upright to prevent the air mixing with the liquid. Care also had to be taken to screen it from the sun or fires. Because of its extreme sensitivity and convenient size, it was often used for marine observations, but by 1885 it was only rarely used owing to the ease with which it could be put out of adjustment when being moved.

However, it was still used for the purposes of comparison and was often mounted on the cases of marine barometers in place of the thermometer, as illustrated in *Fig.* 230. They were also occasionally made for the mantelpiece, in conjunction with clocks, for the amateur weather forecaster, as shown in *Fig.* 279.

219

13

Admiral Fitzroy Barometers

The very considerable contribution that Admiral Robert Fitzroy (1805–65) (*Fig.* 280) made to the development of the marine barometer is outlined in chapter 8. He was also responsible for the fishery or sea coast barometers discussed in chapter 9. He also specialised in weather forecasting and produced rules which depended not only on the height and trend of the barometer but also on the direction and velocity of the wind. These became known as Fitzroy's Rules and in 1862 he published his *Weather Book*. This was a very comprehensive guide to all things relating to the weather, with emphasis on the fact that the state of the air, as shown by the barometer, tells coming rather than present weather conditions.

The success of this book was probably the highlight of the Admiral's career, and his most famous weather rhyme – 'Long foretold, long last; short notice, soon past. Fast rise after low, foretells stronger blow' – was engraved or printed on thousands of barometers during the second half of the nineteenth century. Some makers were so impressed with his weather rules and remarks that they produced barometers with large ivory or paper plates so that they could include some of his rules and remarks on them.

Fig. 281 illustrates a barometer made around 1860 by J. B. Dancer who was an optical, mathematical and philosophical instrument-maker at 13 Cross Street, Manchester, between 1838 and 1860. The case is of rosewood with a glazed door and all the register plates and scales are of ivory. There are two verniers giving readings to one-hundredth of an inch and Admiral Fitzroy's scale words are used, which are identical to those in *Fig.* 245. A wet and dry bulb hygrometer is on the left of the tube and there is a minimum and maximum thermometer on the right. Above the thermometer are remarks from Admiral Fitzroy on weather forecasting and above the hygrometer is a table to assist in foretelling the probable condition of the weather by observing the state of the barometer in conjunction with the direction of the wind. The system is carefully explained and an example is given. A large diameter bulb cistern tube is used for accuracy and the barometer was obviously made for an enthusiastic amateur weather forecaster.

A very interesting instrument called 'The World's Barometer and Weather Indicator' is illustrated in *Fig.* 282. It was devised by James Walter, Major, 4th Lancashire Artillery V and made by Wilson, Son & Walter, Liverpool,

Fig. 280   Admiral Robert Fitzroy (1805–65).

221

around 1862. The case is of carved mahogany with a glazed brass door and there is a boxwood cistern with a leather base within the gilded cistern cover. The overall base is of printed paper on which are mounted the barometer ivory register plates, a sympiesometer on the left and a minimum and maximum thermometer on the right, both with ivory plates. There are two verniers and adjacent to the plates, which cover 27 to 31 inches, there are 'Weather Predictions' for a Rising Scale and a Falling Scale, also Admiral Fitzroy's Rules for 'Rise' and 'Fall' conditions.

Below these predictions are all kinds of meteorological facts, including information on the barometer, sympiesometer and thermometer. There are also twelve monthly tables covering the period 1841 to 1861 giving various meteorological observations, complete with explanatory text. These may well have come from Fitzroy's *Weather Book,* which he published in 1862, and this barometer could be one of the first to be made using Fitzroy's famous weather rules and remarks. Its height is 47½ inches.

By far the best known type of barometer ever produced is illustrated in *Fig.* 283 and headed 'Admiral Fitzroy's Barometer'. It was the first cheap and serviceable barometer made by mass-production methods, and identical instruments, except for variations in the pediment carving and words used, were made in very large numbers.

It is not clear when the first Admiral Fitzroy's barometer was produced, although it is claimed that it was constructed on a plan suggested by Fitzroy, but whether it was made before or after his death in 1865 remains in doubt. The design does not appear to have been registered at the Patent Office but on 11 September 1878 a J. Witherspoon registered a patent No. 3601 relating to the cases of the Fitzroy barometers. He suggested that a small door be made in the side or back of the frame to enable a plug to be fixed in the cistern when the instrument is prepared for transit, the door preferably made to close against a beading to prevent dust entering the interior.

This proves that the Fitzroy barometer was made well before 1878 and, as it was named after the Admiral, it must be assumed that he at least inspired the maker. It could have been called Admiral Fitzroy's barometer because his words were used as weather indications on the scale and his Rising and Falling remarks were recorded below the scale.

Confusion could have arisen between this barometer and the fishery or sea coast barometer (see chapter 9) which used Fitzroy's words on the register plates. The most convincing evidence to suggest that they were not made until after the Admiral's death is that those that appear to be the earliest are headed 'Barometer by the late Admiral Fitzroy'.

The barometer shown in *Fig.* 283 has a carved oak case 50 inches high. The two pointers, which enable comparative readings to be taken, can be adjusted by the two keys on the frame. A reading can be taken to one-tenth of an inch and the bulb cistern, which forms the short limb, has a much larger diameter than the tube to reduce the capacity error. The printed paper weather indications are those suggested by Admiral Fitzroy and below these are two columns of his 'Remarks' on weather interpretation; the left-hand side is for a rising barometer and the right-hand side for a falling barometer.

Fig. 281 Bulb cistern barometer, wet and dry bulb hygrometer and maximum and minimum thermometer in rosewood case by Dancer, Optician, Manchester, c. 1860 (*Peter D. Bosson, Wilmslow*).
Fig. 282 The World's Barometer and Weather Indicator with sympiesometer and minimum and maximum thermometer in carved mahogany case by Wilson Son & Walter, Liverpool, c. 1865 (*Patric Capon, London*).

RISING

1st. A steady rising barometer, which, when continued, shows very fine weather.

2nd. In winter the rise of the barometer presages frost.

3rd. In wet weather, if the mercury rise high, and remain so expect fine weather, but if the mercury rise suddenly very high, fine weather will not last long.

4th. A rapid rise in the barometer indicates unsettled weather, a slow movement the contrary.

N.B. The barometer rises highest of all for north and east wind. The mercury falls lowest for wind and rain together, next to that for wind except it be an east or north-east wind.

FALLING

1st. If a fall takes place with a rising thermometer, wind and rain may be expected from the south-eastward, southward or south-westward.

2nd. A fall with a low thermometer foretells snow or rain.

3rd. A sudden fall of the barometer with westerly wind is generally followed by a violent storm from N.W. or N.E.

4th. A rapid fall indicates wind or wind and rain.

5th. In very hot weather the fall of the mercury denotes thunder or a sudden fall indicates high wind.

Indications of approaching changes are shewn less by the height of the barometer than by its falling or rising.

Thus the figures are of more importance than the words.

The lower half of the case is veneered in oak with a Fahrenheit spirit thermometer on a silvered brass scale on the right and a storm-glass or chemical weather-glass on the left. This curious device has been in existence for more than two hundred years and was offered for sale at a shop 'Under the Goat and Compasses' on old London Bridge. The name of the inventor is unknown, but some attribute the honour to an Italian sailor, whilst others say that it was discovered by accident by some old alchemists who were constantly experimenting with the substances composing the solution with which it is made.

It is simply a glass bottle, about 10 inches long and hermetically sealed, containing crystals of potassium nitrate and ammonium chloride in an alcoholic solution of camphor with some distilled water. It is claimed to be helpful in prognosticating changes in the weather, particularly high winds, storms or tempests. In fine weather the crystals are said to settle at the bottom of the tube, while in stormy weather they are said to rise, making the solution turbid. There are certainly changes in the appearance of the solution from time to time, but they are more likely to be from light, heat or the electrical state of the atmosphere.

The storm-glass is really an irregular form of thermometric barometer. It

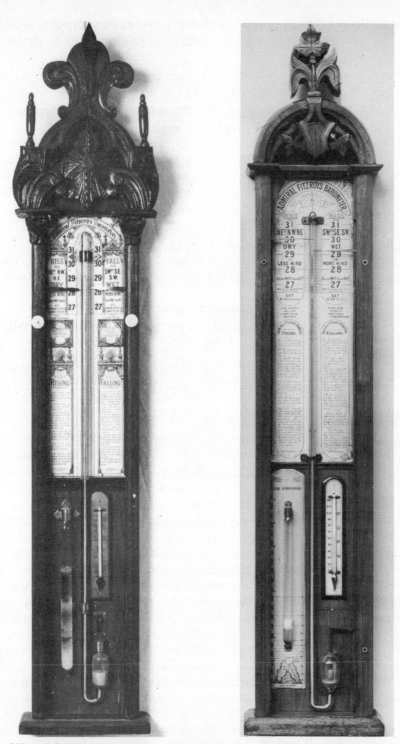

Fig. 283　Admiral Fitzroy's barometer with thermometer and storm-glass in carved oak case, c. 1870.
Fig. 284　Admiral Fitzroy's barometer in carved oak case, c. 1875.

must be nicely balanced as to the solubility of the camphor and salts and there are several formulas; two that are reasonably satisfactory are as follows:

3 fluid oz.	Water
2 fluid oz.	Absolute alcohol (100%)
½ dram (avoirdupois)	Ammonium chloride
½ dram (avoirdupois)	Potassium nitrate
2 drams (avoirdupois)	Camphor
2 grams	Camphor
0.5 grams	Potassium nitrate
0.5 grams	Ammonium chloride
28.5 ml	Alcohol
28.5 ml	Distilled water

Dissolve the camphor in the alcohol and the salts in the water, then gradually add the alcohol solution of camphor to the aqueous solution with constant shaking. The changes in the solution are said to signify the following:

Clear liquid − Bright weather.

Crystals at bottom − Thick air, frost in winter.

Dim liquid − Rain.

Dim liquid with small stars − Thunderstorms.

Large flakes − Heavy air, overcast sky, snow in winter.

Threads in upper portion of liquid − Windy weather.

Small dots − Damp weather, fog.

Rising flakes which remain high − Wind in the upper air regions.

Small stars − In winter on bright, sunny days, snow in one or two days.

The higher the crystals rise in the glass tube in winter the colder it will be. All the foregoing is empirical.

This barometer is portable as it has a check valve at the bottom of the bulb cistern. This consists of a cork attached to the end of a brass rod which is connected to a brass plate fixed to the base. The cork can be raised and lowered by a brass lever at the back of the barometer for the purpose of plugging the mercury in the tube whilst in transit. The lever can be locked in the lowered position by applying a catch.

Fig. 284 shows a carved oak Fitzroy barometer made about five years later. The Fahrenheit mercury thermometer has an ivory scale and the barometer can be made portable by operating a toothed bar with a key through the hole adjacent to the cistern. There is a blue-coloured diagram under the storm-glass and this has two scales; on the left is the 'Height of Atmosphere in Miles', up to 45 miles, and on the right the 'Height of Mercury in Inches' down to 1 inch. The mountains depicted are the Andes and the Himalayas, and an explanation is printed after the 'Rising' remarks:

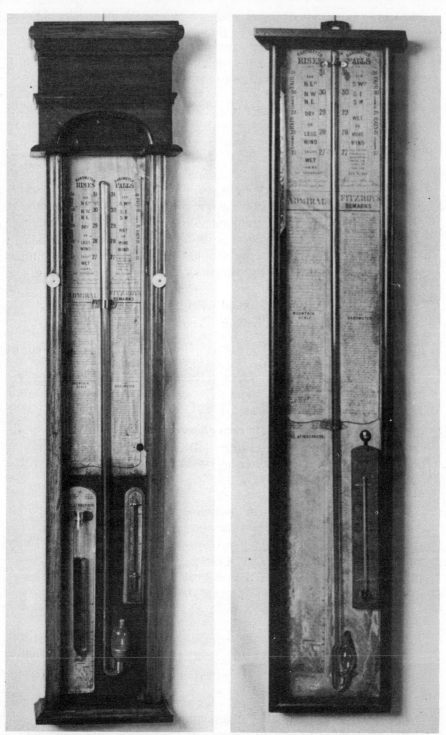

Fig. 285 Admiral Fitzroy's barometer with thermometer and storm-glass in oak case. Not portable, c. 1875. *Fig.* 286 Admiral Fitzroy's barometer with thermometer in mahogany case, c. 1880.

227

The scale on one side of the diagram beneath shows the height of the Mercury at different elevations, thus at the top of Ben Nevis the Mercury stands at about twenty-five inches, at the top of Mont Blanc about seventeen inches and at the summit of the Himalayas, five and a half miles in altitude, at only eleven inches.

A quite early Fitzroy barometer in a plain mahogany case is illustrated in *Fig.* 286. The instrument has no storm-glass, but the Admiral's words on the mountain scale and the barometer are interesting:

Mountain Scale
Air being a substance possessing gravity it necessarily presses downwards in the direction of the centre of the earth and therefore the degree of pressure on any given point will be equal to the column of air above that point and proportional to its density. The atmosphere is of the greatest vertical height at the level of the sea and here its pressure is about fifteen pounds on every square inch of surface, which pressure is exerted in every direction.

The scale on one side of the diagram indicates the height of the mercury at different elevations, thus at the top of Ben Nevis the mercury stands at about twenty-five inches, at the top of Mont Blanc about seventeen inches, and at the summit of the Himalayas, five and a half miles in altitude, at only eleven inches.

When the state of the weather appears to disagree with any great change of the barometer, such change may be looked for with double force at no great distance off. Thus in May 1857 in and around London, the mercury which had been lowering for some days began to rise with but ¾ inch rain (per rain gauge) whilst Reading in Berkshire only 30 miles off was visited by a storm so severe as almost to form an event in the annals of the town.

The Barometer
Is one of the most valuable instruments ever contrived for investigating the nature and laws of the wonderful ocean of air in which we live. The atmosphere which envelopes the earth on every side extends to a height of about forty-five miles, diminishing in density from the sea level upwards. In the diagram below is a representation of the atmosphere divided by horizontal lines into thirty spaces each containing an equal quantity of air.

The lower layers however are so greatly compressed by the weight of those above them that the lower half of the atmosphere lies within four miles of the sea level, while the upper half is so much expanded as to occupy upwards of forty miles.

The following are the principal laws of air:
1st.   Its pressure is equal in all directions.
2nd.   Its degree of pressure depends on the vertical height and is in proportion to its density.

228

3rd.   It affords support according to its density and to the weight of fluid displaced.

Thus the figures are of more importance than the words.

It can be seen that Admiral Fitzroy's barometer, with its information on the atmosphere and short treatise on meteorology, is a very interesting and collectable instrument and it is not surprising that a very large number were sold and that it remained popular into the twentieth century. The cases were usually made of oak, but sometimes mahogany or beech was used; the majority were rectangular and plain, but some pediments were richly carved whilst inlay and marquetry was occasionally used.

Fig. 287 shows an Admiral Fitzroy's barometer in a plain oak case. It has an interesting printed paper plate with Gothic-style decoration and a design registration mark in the form of a lozenge, showing that the design was registered with the British Patent Office in August 1881. These marks were used on English ceramics, metalwork and furniture between 1842 and 1883, and were impressed, printed or applied as a wafer. On this barometer it is printed below 'Admiral Fitzroy's Barometer' and on the left of the mark is '367' and on the right '815'. The barometer was probably made around 1885 and is 37 inches in height.

A similar barometer, made by John G. Murdock & Co. Ltd, of London and Melbourne, is illustrated in *Fig.* 288. The case is again of solid oak and the pediment has been extended to allow for an eight-day clock to be included. This instrument is portable as it has a check valve operated from the back of the case.

Below Fitzroy's remarks are the words 'Entered at Stationers Hall'. This relates to the hall of the 'Masters and Keepers or Wardens and Commonalty of the Mystery or Art of the Stationers of the City of London'. The Company was incorporated in 1557 and had, until the passing of the Copyright Act in 1842, an absolute monopoly, as all printers were obliged to serve an apprenticeship to a member of the Company and every publication from a Bible to a ballad was required to be 'Entered at Stationers Hall'. This registration is no longer compulsory, but is still useful in making good claims of copyright.

A popular case design is illustrated in *Fig.* 289. It is made of oak and the early cases of this type had a fixing blacksmith's nail at each corner of the frame. There are two manually operated indicating pointers and the spirit Fahrenheit thermometer has a boxwood scale. This barometer is portable as it has an iron tap, just below the cistern, which is operated from the back of the case.

Towards the end of the nineteenth century a plain and cheap Fitzroy barometer was produced and an example is given in *Fig.* 290. It has a solid mahogany case with one brass manually operated pointer to read the scale, which is compensated for capacity error. A storm-glass is not fitted but it has, unusually, the maker's or retailer's name printed in its place 'M. E. Solomons, Optician, Nassau Street, Dublin'.

This type of barometer is still easily obtainable, and instruments can be

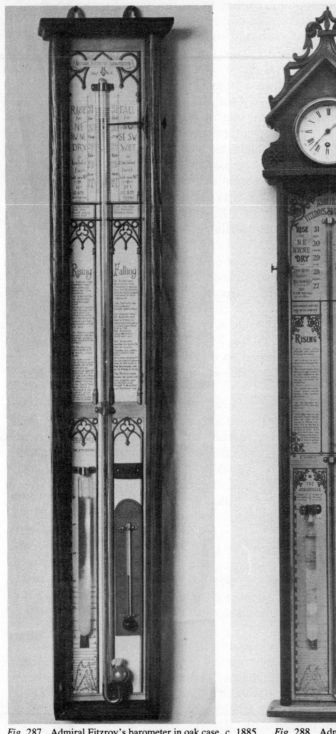

Fig. 287   Admiral Fitzroy's barometer in oak case, c. 1885.   *Fig.* 288   Admiral Fitzroy's barometer
with clock in oak case, c. 1885.

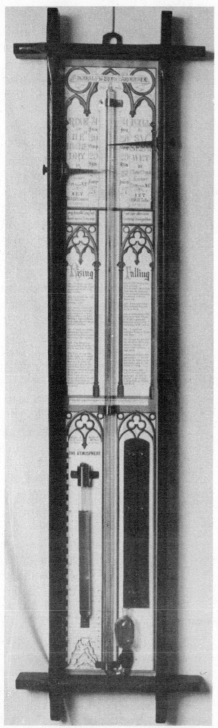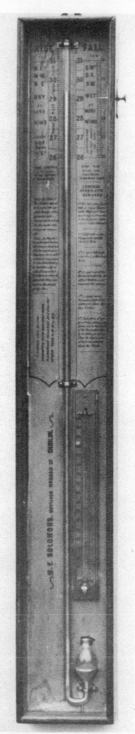

Fig. 289   Admiral Fitzroy's barometer with iron portable tap, c. 1890.   *Fig.* 290   Admiral Fitzroy's barometer with thermometer in mahogany case, c. 1895.

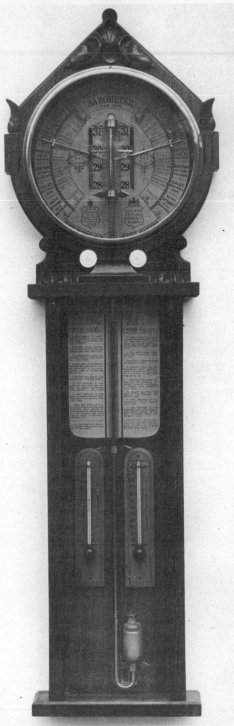

found with a selection of words used for Admiral Fitzroy's remarks. They all have thermometers, usually with a boxwood scale, but some do not have mountain scales or storm-glasses.

An interesting and distinctive bulb cistern barometer, known as the Royal Polytechnic barometer, is shown in *Fig.* 291. The sole manufacturer in England was Joseph Davis & Co., Royal Polytechnic Institution, Kennington Park Road, London, who produced them between 1870 and 1885. The paper register plates have the Royal Coat of Arms and the Prince of Wales Feathers; they are also annotated 'Design Copyright and Title Registered', but were also made under licence in various other countries.

The glazed case is made of oak and everything is symmetrical except for the tube. Fahrenheit and centigrade thermometers are fitted below Admiral Fitzroy's special remarks for rising and falling conditions and these are similar to the words on the Fitzroy barometers already described. The two ivory keys, below the circular dial, control pointers each side of the tube to which are attached hands that indicate the weather conditions listed round the

Fig. 291   Royal Polytechnic barometer in carved oak case by Joseph Davis & Co., London, c. 1880.

dial. These cover seven winter and eight summer possible weather combinations from 'Very fine with frost' to 'Very stormy with heavy gales'. The action of setting the pointer against the level of the mercury automatically moves the hand to one of the weather signs which predicts the approaching weather. There are two sets of pointers and hands so that daily comparisons of the reading can be made.

Some of these barometers have enclosed cases with a single thermometer and some have seven small segment dials, set below the main dial, so that daily readings can be recorded for a week at a time.

14

Other Cistern Barometers

A very unusual early bulb cistern barometer signed 'Isaac Robelou: Fecit: Londini, 1719' is illustrated in *Fig.* 292. The base board is decorated with Chinese lacquer work and the moulded edges are coloured red with gold ornamentation. The weather indications are in Latin and English and the scale has 36 divisions. The spirit thermometer has an unusual scale with zero at 'Temperate Weather', extending upwards to 90 'Excessive Hot Weather' and downwards to 90 'Excessive Cold Weather'. There is a manual pointer on a brass wire.

Stick barometers with bulb cisterns were rare during the eighteenth century although they were popular on the Continent.

One of the very few extant barometers by George Graham (*Fig.* 293) made around 1720 is illustrated in *Fig.* 294. The right-hand pillar of the architecturally designed frame supports a barometer which has floral engraving on the register plates, and this is repeated on the clips retaining the tube. Summer and winter weather indications are engraved but there are no figures. The left-hand pillar supports a spirit thermometer with a scale almost identical to the one used on the Robelou barometer. This is the first scale devised by G. D. Fahrenheit (1686–1736) in 1710 and covered 90° Blood Heat, 0° Temperate and −90° Freezing point of a mixture of salt, water and ice.

The centre of the arch supports a cat-gut hygrometer which is held taut by a lead weight below the dial; the gut is protected by a tapering walnut case and it winds and unwinds with changes in humidity which are recorded on the dial.

Honest George Graham – as he was known – was born in Cumberland and tramped to London as a boy when he could just about read and write. He was apprenticed in 1688 to Henry Aske and became a member of the Clockmakers' Company in 1695. He became one of Thomas Tompion's assistants in 1696 and, having married his niece, became his partner in 1711. Tompion died in 1713 and Graham succeeded to the business. He became the leading maker of clocks and spent his life in scientific enquiry and the manufacture of suitable astronomical instruments for the Astronomer Royal of Greenwich Observatory. One of them, James Bradley, wrote of him:

I am sensible that, if my own endeavours have, in any respect been

effectual to the advancement of Astronomy, it has principally been owing to the advice and assistance given to me by our worthy member, Mr. George Graham, whose great skill and judgement in mechanics, joined with a complete and practical knowledge of the uses of astronomical instruments enabled him to contrive and execute them in the most perfect manner.

When Graham died in 1751 he was buried in Westminster Abbey in the same grave as Tompion. The memorial stone reads:

The body of George Graham of London, Watchmaker and F.R.S. whose curious inventions do honour to the British Genius whose accurate performances are the standard of Mechanic Skill.

A few clockmakers incorporated barometers into the doors of their long-case clocks and an example is given in *Fig.* 295. It is a cistern barometer with silvered brass register plates engraved with summer and winter weather indications but no figures. The plates are decorated with leaf scrolls and wheat-ear borders; P. Sullivan, London, is engraved below the scale. He is recorded as working at Wickham Court, London between 1738 and 1743.

The clock is housed in a mahogany case and was made by Christopher Pinchbeck of Cockspur Street, London, who called himself 'Senior' clockmaker to the King. He was the son of Christopher Pinchbeck, a celebrated maker of astronomical and musical clocks, and inventor of a zinc-copper alloy resembling gold and called 'Pinchbeck'.

The red walnut cased grandfather clock shown in *Fig.* 296 has a cistern tube barometer incorporated in the door. It has a carved scroll pediment with egg-and-dart

Fig. 292 Bulb cistern barometer in Chinese lacquer case by Isaac Robelou, Londini, 1719 (British Crown Copyright, *Science Museum, London*).

Fig. 293   George Graham (1673–1751).

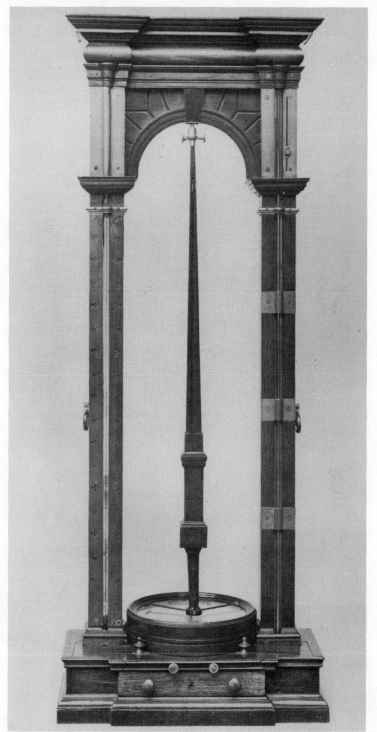

Fig. 294 Barometer, thermometer and hygrometer in a walnut frame by George Graham, London, c. 1720 (British Crown Copyright, *Science Museum, London*).

Fig. 295   Clock/barometer in mahogany case by P. Sullivan, London, c. 1740 (*Christies, London*).
Fig. 296   Clock/barometer in red walnut case by Sam Hollyer, London, c. 1820 (*Sotheby's, Chester*).

moulding on each side of the silvered brass register plates. The barometer tube is exposed and a flat round turned cistern cover is used. It was made around 1820 by Sam Hollyer of London.

15

Care of the Stick or
Cistern Tube Barometer

It is probably true to say that one of the most important things to know about a barometer is how to handle it. Aneroid barometers are reasonably robust, but mercurial ones, particularly those with an open cistern, must be handled with great care or the mercury in the tube may be so displaced that it becomes necessary to refill the tube. This can only be undertaken by a specialist restorer who has the equipment to evacuate the tube.

The most delicate barometers are the very few which still have an open cistern, as illustrated in *Fig.* 8 (chapter 2). It must be kept in a vertical or near vertical position and not be subjected to any abrupt movement whatsoever, as this could well result in a loss of mercury in the cistern and, possibly, air bubbles in the tube. A lowering of the level of mercury in the cistern will distort the barometer reading, as it will record a lower figure, but this can be corrected by topping up the mercury in the cistern using another barometer for comparison.

To get rid of air bubbles in the tube it is necessary to remove the tube from the cistern, after plugging the open end with a finger, and then invert it. By gently shaking the tube, it should be possible to eliminate the bubbles; the mercury should then be topped up in the tube which can then be returned to the cistern.

Before any stick barometer is transported it is advisable to remove the cistern cover in order to determine the type of cistern used. Closed cistern tube barometers are less vulnerable to damage as the mercury cannot be spilt, unless there is a fissure between the tube and the boxwood cistern, or a split has occurred in the leather base of the cistern; in either case the repair should be carried out by a professional restorer.

Almost all closed cistern barometers are fitted with portable screws and, before transit, the screw should always be applied so that all the air is removed from the cistern and the tube is completely full of mercury. It is preferable to incline the barometer at an angle of 45° before turning the screw, as this will allow the mercury to rise freely to the top of the tube and reduce the pressure on the screw whilst being turned. The barometer can then be carried or rested in any position.

There is one danger, however, in doing this; if the leather is very old it may have become brittle with age and there is a possibility that the screw pad may damage or puncture the leather when screwed against it. If there is a danger of this happening then it is probably better to carry the barometer in a horizontal position.

Closed cistern tube barometers without portable screws should be carried or transported in this position so that the mercury is always at the top of the tube; this prevents the mercury from rising and falling in the tube whilst in motion and stops air bubbles gaining access to the tube. If the mercury is allowed to rise too sharply its force against the top of the tube could break the glass.

Bulb cistern stick barometers can be carried carefully at an angle of 45°, but they should never be laid flat as mercury will spill from the bulb cistern and air bubbles may appear in the tube. The mercury lost from the cistern can be replaced, but it is difficult to remove the air bubbles and the tube will most probably have to be refilled. When this type of barometer has to be moved any great distance it is advisable to plug the tube at least with a cork and handle it carefully.

A better idea is to obtain a plug which consists of a short piece of wire with wool wound round one end and a movable cork at the other. Before plugging the tube the barometer should be inclined so that the mercury rises to the top of the tube; the wool end of the wire is then forced into the tube where the bore narrows near the bend and is kept in this position by sliding the cork down the wire until it is firmly fixed into the opening of the bulb cistern. The wool prevents the mercury in the tube from returning to the cistern, whilst the cork prevents the mercury left in the cistern from escaping. With the plug firmly in position the barometer can be carried or positioned at any angle.

When moving double- or multiple-tube barometers, care must be taken to tilt them slowly so that the mercury and, particularly, the second liquid is given time to settle in its new position. They should be carried or transported at an angle of about 45°. Sympiesometers should be moved in a vertical position to prevent the gas forming bubbles in the liquid.

If it is found, by comparison or otherwise, that a cistern tube barometer is not recording a correct reading, the mercury should first be examined. If there are no air bubbles present, which is evidenced by breaks in the mercury, the tube should be inclined to one side – gradually at first – to see whether the mercury rises to the top of the tube with a dull thud which vibrates the tube. If this happens it can be assumed that there is a good vacuum, but if there is no thud or the mercury fails to reach the top of the tube, it indicates that air has penetrated the vacuum and the tube should be replaced. If the tube is functioning correctly the reading can be adjusted by the portable screw, or by raising or lowering the tube by adding to, or removing, some of the packing in the cistern housing. On a few early barometers it is possible to raise or lower the register plates. With bulb cisterns an adjustment can be made by raising or lowering the level of mercury in the cistern.

Great care should be taken when using mercury as it is poisonous. It is sensible to wash your hands after using it and it should not be left exposed to vaporise. It does not affect wood, but it is advisable to recover any mercury that has been spilt in the workshop and to keep it in a closed container. Mercury forms an amalgam with many metals so it should not be handled when wearing gold or silver rings.

The general restoration of barometers is outside the scope of this book, but the care of the various silvered dials and register plates should be mentioned. Silvering that is discoloured may be restored satisfactorily by brushing with cream of tartar and water on a very soft brush. It will have no effect on the waxed lettering, but may wash off any painted letters. If this does not bring back the surface to an acceptable standard the dial should be resilvered; this should be done by a specialist, but if you would like to try your hand at this you can buy a resilvering compound, with instructions, from a horological supplier.

Dirty ivory register plates and thermometer scales can be cleaned by using the finest flour paper, and scratched ivory can be polished with fine pumice powder and petrol; it can be brought to a pristine state with whiting powder and methylated spirit applied with a felt pad. Yellowed ivory can be bleached by exposing it to sunlight.

The woodwork needs little attention other than normal dusting and an occasional careful polish with a soft cloth.

Bibliography

Adams, George, 'A Short Dissertation on the Barometer, Thermometer and other Meteorological Instruments' (London, 1790).

Baillie, G. H., *Watchmakers and Clockmakers of the World,* 3rd edn (N.A.G. Press Ltd, London, 1974).

Banfield, Edwin, *Antique Barometers: an Illustrated Survey* (Wayland Publications, Trowbridge, 1976).

Bell, G. H. and Bell, E. F., *Old English Barometers* (The Wykeham Press, Winchester, 1952).

Bellchambers, J. K., *Somerset Clockmakers* (Antiquarian Horological Society, London, 1968).

Belville, J. H., *A Manual of the Barometer* (London, 1849).

Bolle, Bert, *Barometers* (Argus Books Ltd, Watford, 1982).

Britten, F. J., *Old Watches and Clocks and their Makers,* 5th edn (London, 1922).

Bryden, D. J., 'Balthazar Knie, a provincial barometer maker', *Connoisseur,* March 1972.

Bryden, D. J., *Scottish Scientific Instrument-Makers, 1600–1900* (Royal Scottish Museum, Edinburgh, 1972).

Daumas, Maurice, *Scientific Instruments of the 17th and 18th Centuries and their Makers* (B. T. Batsford Ltd, London, 1972).

Goodison, Nicholas, *English Barometers and their Makers 1680–1860* (Antique Collectors' Club, 1977).

Harris, John, *Lexicon Technicum* (London, 1704–10).

Loomes, Brian, *Watchmakers and Clockmakers of the World,* Volume 2 (N.A.G. Press Ltd, London, 1978).

Middleton, W. E. K., *The History of the Barometer* (The Johns Hopkins Press, Baltimore, 1964).

Negretti & Zambra, *A Treatise on Meteorological Instruments* (London, 1864).

Rees, Abraham, *The Cyclopaedia* (London, 1819).

Saul, Edward, 'An Historical and Philosophical Account of the Barometer or Weather-Glass' (London, 1735).

Smith, John, 'A Complete Discourse of the Nature, Use and Right Managing of that Wonderful Instrument, the Baroscope or Quicksilver Weather Glass' (London, 1688).

Taylor, E. G. R., *The Mathematical Practitioners of Tudor and Stuart England* (Cambridge, 1954).

Taylor, E. G. R., *The Mathematical Practitioners of Hanoverian England* (Cambridge, 1966).

Thoday, A. G., *Barometers* (Science Museum, London, 1978).

Index

ABRAHAM & DANCER   186, 187
ADAMS, Dudley   38, 98, 102, 104
ADAMS, George Snr.   37, 38, 39, 64,
   65, 67
ADAMS, George Jnr.   38, 55, 64, 65,
   67, 76, 77, 82, 83, 84, 131
ADIE, Alexander   93, 214, 215
ADIE, John   216
ADIE, Patrick   171, 172, 177, 178
agricultural barometer   127
AIANO, Charles   94, 95, 118, 119
AMONTONS, Guillaume   208
AYSCOUGH, James   49, 50, 51, 52

BARNY — London   96
BATE, R. B.   120, 122, 169
BAUMBACH, Otto   208, 209
bayonet tube   30
BEILBY — Bristol   91, 92
BELLAMY, A.   88, 90
BELLATTI, L.   160
BENBOW, Thomas   48, 49
BENNETT, John   51
BENNETT, T.   166
BERGE, Matthew   91, 92, 164
BERRINGER — London   101
BIRD, John   51, 52
BLUNT & Son   196, 197
BLUNT, Thomas   73, 98, 99, 100, 143,
   144
BOESE, B.   137, 138
bottle tube   44, 45
BOURDON, Eugene   130
BOYLE, Robert   5, 7, 8, 206
BRANDER, C. G. & SON   176, 178
bulb cistern tube   44, 45
Bunten air trap   171
BURTON, George   63, 64
BUTLER, Edward   94, 95

CAMPBELL, J.   177

CANTI, C. A.   174
CARPENTER & WESLEY   130
CARY, William   91
CASELLA, Louis   119, 127, 129
CHADBURN BROS   130
CHANCELLOR & SON   187, 188
chemical weather glass   224
CHIPPENDALE, Thomas   44
correction for capacities   184
correction for capillary action   184
correction for temperature   184
COX, W. C.   129, 130
CRICHTON, Joseph   215, 216
CUFF, John   40, 41, 146, 149
CUMMINS, C.   215, 216

DANCER, J. B.   186, 220, 223
DAVENPORT, Stephen   31, 32, 34
DAVIS, JOSEPH & SON   133, 134, 232
DAY, F.   93
DE LUC, Jean André   194
DENT, E. J.   130
DENTON, Joseph   96
DESCARTES, René   8
DIXEY, C. W.   130
DOLLOND, George   130
DOLLOND, John   66, 67
DOLLOND — London   106, 110, 138
DOLLOND, Peter   66, 67, 75, 83, 84
double-angle barometer   158
DRING & FAGE   167, 168
DUNN, J.   108

ELLIOTT & SONS   130
ELLIOTT BROS   125, 126
ENGLISH — Brighton   218, 219

FAHRENHEIT, G. D.   34, 234
Fahrenheit thermometer scale   34
farmer's barometer   130
FIELD, H. & SON   130, 132

FINNEY, John 152, 155
fishery barometer 189
FITZROY, Admiral Robert 171, 189,
  192, 220, 221
FLETCHER, J. & SONS 215
floating gauge 67, 82
FORTIN, Nicolas 188
FRANK, James 88

GALILEO, Galilei 2, 4
GALLY, P. 105
GATTY, James 211
GAPP — London 202
GARDNER, J. & J. 103, 106
GARDNERS — Glasgow 106, 107
GAY-LUSSAC, J. L. 203
GLAISHER, James 205
GLANVILL, Joseph 9
GOLD, E. 178, 180
Gold slide 180
GRAHAM, George 19, 51, 234, 236,
  237

HANNY, James 134, 135
HARDY — London 96
HARRIS, A. O. 216, 217
HARRIS, John 19, 142
HARRIS, WILLIAM & SON 130, 216,
  217
HAUKSBEE, Francis 142
HEATH, Thomas 37
HEATH, W. & T. C. 125, 126
HICKS, James J. 134, 136, 175, 176
HOLLYER, Sam 238, 239
HOLMES, William 121
HOOKE, Robert 9, 60, 163, 206
HOWORTH, Charles 111, 112, 114,
  160
HUGHES, H. 108
HUGHES, J. 218
HUGHES — London 110
hygrometer 60

JONES — Dublin 167, 169
JONES, Henry 12, 13
JONES, Oxford St. 98, 101
JONES, Thomas 107, 109, 123, 124,
  165, 167, 201, 203
JORDON, J. B. 211

KNIE, Balthazar 79, 80, 157, 158, 208,
  209

LAINTON, Samuel 111, 114, 160, 161
LANGFORD, William 129, 130
LEGH, Richard 11
LINNELL, J. 152, 155
LUND, W. 125

MACRAE — London 91, 92
MANN, James 40, 41, 49
MANTICHA, Dominick 85, 86, 211
MARINE INSTRUMENTS LTD. 178,
  179
MARRATT, John 122, 123, 130
MARSHALL, John 19
MARTIN, Benjamin 57, 58, 59, 60, 61
MELLING & CO. 170
MERLE, William 2
MILLER, J. 194, 195
millibar scale 178
miner's barometer 131
model barometer 134, 135
MOLINER, Charles 81, 159
MOORE, Jonas 11
MORLAND, Samuel 140, 141
MURDOCK, JOHN G. & CO.
  LTD. 229

NAIRNE & BLUNT 74, 75, 76, 98,
  194, 195, 196, 197
NAIRNE, Edward 51, 72, 73, 74, 163
NEGRETTI & ZAMBRA 123, 124,
  125, 130, 132, 137, 138, 152, 153,
  161, 162, 173, 174, 178, 179, 180,
  187, 189, 204, 212, 213
NEGRETTI, Enrico (Henry) 125, 201,
  203
NEGRETTY & CO. 117
NEILL BROTHERS 168
neutral point 184
NEVE, Richard 30
NEWMAN, John Frederick 110, 130,
  181, 182, 185, 186, 199, 200, 202
NORTH, Francis 12
NORTH, Roger 12

ORME, Charles 145, 146, 147
OWENS — Liverpool 217, 219

PASTORELLI, Joseph 105
PATRICK, John 18, 19, 26, 28, 30, 34,
  142, 163
PEDRALIO, Baptista 159

PEDUZZY, JOSEPH & CO.   117
PILLISCHER, M.   130
PINCHBECK, Christopher   235
pit barometer   131
PIZZALA, F. A.   130
POLTI, T. L.   87, 90
POZZI, J.   109
PURCHEON, George   111, 114, 116
PYEFINCH, Henry   67, 68, 69, 70

QUARE, Daniel   19, 20, 22, 23, 24, 26,
   28, 142

RABALIO   77, 211, 212
RAMSDEN, Jesse   51, 54, 55, 67, 82,
   83, 197
REAUMUR, René A. F. de   107
Réaumur thermometer scale   107
RITTSON, J.   55, 56
ROBB, William   76, 80, 157, 158
ROBELOU, Isaac   234, 235
RONCHETI, Bapt.   94, 95, 159
RONCHETI, BAPT & CO.   158, 160,
   210, 211
RONKETTI, J. M.   87, 90
ROSS, Andrew   130, 189, 190
ROUTLEDGE, Adam   111, 112
Royal Polytechnic barometer   232
Royal Society thermometer scale   30
RUBERGALL, THOMAS   103, 104,
   109
RUSSELL, John   97, 98

SALA, Dominico   211
SALLA, J. Bapt.   93, 94
SAUL, Edward   34, 144
SCARLETT, Edward   40, 42, 43, 144
sea coast barometer   189
SEWILL, J.   172
SILBERRAD, Charles   211
SILO, R.   172
SISSON, Jeremiah   51, 54, 55
SISSON, Jonathan   37, 51, 55
SMITH, Addison   147
SMITH — Bath   81
SMITH, John   16, 140
SOLOMONS, M. E.   229

SOMALVICO & CO.   130
SOMALVICO, V . & SON   124
SPENCER BROWNING & CO.   167,
   168, 169
SPENCER BROWNING & RUST   216
SQUIRE, P.   122
STENSON, John   26
STEWARD, J. H.   134, 135
storm-glass   224
SULLIVAN, P.   235, 238

TAGLIABUE, Caesar   117, 119
TARONE — Bristol   103, 104
TARTS — London   61, 62
THOMSON, Thomas   208, 209
TOMPION, Thomas   24, 26
TORRE   211
TORRICELLI, Evangelista   4, 5, 6, 10
TROUGHTON & SIMMS   70, 198, 200
TROUGHTON, Edward   70
TROUGHTON, J. & E.   70, 81, 82
TROUGHTON, John   51, 70, 71
TROUGHTON, J. & J.   70, 71

VERNIER, Pierre   49
Vernier scale   49
VERRIER, James   45, 46

WALTER, James   220
WALKER, I. & A.   170
WATKINS & HILL   118, 119, 130
WATKINS & SMITH   147, 150, 151
WATKINS, Francis   76, 77, 78, 147
WEBB — Taunton   126
WELSH, John   171
WEST — London   44, 46
wet and dry bulb hygrometer   130
WHITEHURST, John   156
WHITEHURST, M. J.   158
WILSON SON & WALTER   220, 223
WISKER, John   100
WOLLER, Mathew   87, 90
WYNNE, Henry   12, 13, 14

YARWELL, John   19

ZAPPA, C.   105